2 a)   10 km *[1 mark]*
   b)   0.8 metres per second *[1 mark]*
   c)   Saltation *[1 mark]*

You could also have said traction — pebbles will be rolled along the river bed before they start to saltate.

   d)   Between 20 and 30 km the river's velocity drops *[1 mark]*. When rivers slow down they deposit the material they are carrying *[1 mark]*.
   e)   E.g. velocity is low in the upper course because of friction from the rough channel sides and bed *[1 mark]*. Velocity increases along the river's course because the channel's sides get smoother so there's less friction *[1 mark]*.
   f)   Any one from: e.g. the channel could be deepened through hydraulic action *[1 mark]*, which is when the force of the water breaks rock particles away from the river channel *[1 mark]*. / The channel could be worn away by abrasion *[1 mark]*, which is when eroded rocks picked up by the river scrape and rub against the channel *[1 mark]*.

Pages 17-19: River Landforms

1 a)   633524 *[1 mark]*
   b)   Waterfall Y *[1 mark]*

Remember that the steeper the gradient, the closer together the contour lines will be.

   c)   E.g. waterfalls form where a river flows over an area of hard rock followed by an area of softer rock *[1 mark]*, so the Afon Merch must flow over rocks with alternating hardness *[1 mark]*.
   d)   A gorge forms as a waterfall retreats up a river channel *[1 mark]*. The hard rock cap is undercut by erosion (abrasion) so it becomes unsupported and collapses *[1 mark]*. Over time, more undercutting causes more collapses, so the waterfall retreats, forming a gorge *[1 mark]*.
2 a)   Any two from: there are interlocking spurs *[1 mark]*. / The gradient of the river channel is steep *[1 mark]*. / The valley has steep sides *[1 mark]*. / The valley is V-shaped *[1 mark]*. / The river channel is narrow *[1 mark]*.
   b)   E.g. the landscape in Figure 2 is probably an area of resistant rock *[1 mark]*. This is less easily eroded by the river, which is why the valley sides are steep/interlocking spurs have formed *[1 mark]*.
3 a) i)   A *[1 mark]*
    ii)   During a flood, eroded material is deposited over the whole flood plain *[1 mark]*. The heaviest material is deposited closest to the river channel, because it gets dropped first when the river slows down *[1 mark]*. Over time, the deposited material builds up, creating levees along the edges of the channel *[1 mark]*.
   b)   When the river floods onto the flood plain, the water slows down and deposits the eroded material that it's transporting *[1 mark]*, so if the river floods repeatedly, the flood plain builds up *[1 mark]*.
4 a) i)   A river cliff is likely to be found at A *[1 mark]*. The current is faster on the outside bend of the meander because the channel is deeper *[1 mark]*. This means there's more erosion on the outside bend, so a river cliff is formed *[1 mark]*.
    ii)   Any two from: abrasion *[1 mark]* / hydraulic action *[1 mark]* / solution *[1 mark]*
   b)   A point bar is likely to be found at B *[1 mark]*. The current is slower on the inside bend of the meander because the river channel is shallower *[1 mark]*. This means material is deposited on the inside of the bend, so a point bar is formed *[1 mark]*.
   c)   E.g. continued erosion could cause the outside bends of the meander to get closer together *[1 mark]* until there's only a small bit of land left between the bend *[1 mark]*. The river could break through this narrow bit of land (usually during a flood) and flow along the shortest course between the bends *[1 mark]*. Deposition would eventually cut off the meander, forming an ox-bow lake *[1 mark]*.

Page 20: Climate, Weather

1 a)   Any one from: e.g. a stor[...] to burst its banks *[1 mark]*, depositing material to form levees *[1 mark]*. / The increased volume and velocity of a river during a storm could cause the river to break through the neck of a meander *[1 mark]*, eventually forming an ox-bow lake *[1 mark]*.

You could also mention that a flood caused by a storm could lead to more material being deposited on the flood plain, building it up over time.

   b)   E.g. during a drought there is less rainfall than usual, so the water volume in the river drops *[1 mark]*. This means that the river has less energy, so less erosion and transportation occur *[1 mark]*.
2 a)   Any one from: e.g. wet weather would cause high rates of chemical weathering *[1 mark]*, as carbonation and dissolution weathering happen when rainwater comes into contact with the minerals in rocks *[1 mark]*. / Cooler temperatures would reduce the rate of chemical weathering *[1 mark]* as chemical reactions happen faster at higher temperatures *[1 mark]*.
   b)   Any two from: e.g. the wet climate means more water enters the river channel, so there is a higher discharge *[1 mark]*. This means the river has more power for vertical erosion, forming the V-shaped valleys in Figure 2 *[1 mark]*. / The wet climate means that the ground can become saturated and unstable *[1 mark]*, which may have caused mass movements, e.g. slumping and rockfalls, along the course of the river *[1 mark]*. / In winter, cold temperatures may lead to freeze-thaw weathering *[1 mark]*. This can loosen rock material, adding to the river's load and helping to form V-shaped valleys *[1 mark]*.

Pages 21-22: River Flooding

1 a) i)   E.g. in urban areas, there are lots of impermeable surfaces such as concrete, which prevent rain from infiltrating the soil *[1 mark]*. Deforestation/clearing vegetation reduces the interception of rainfall by plants and infiltration by the soil *[1 mark]*. Reduced infiltration and interception mean that there is more surface runoff and river discharge, making flooding more likely *[1 mark]*.
    ii)   E.g. the relief of the landscape could increase flood risk *[1 mark]*, because there are quite a lot of upland areas in the drainage basin, so rainfall on these slopes would rapidly reach the river by surface runoff *[1 mark]*.
   b)   E.g. after a long period of rain, the soil becomes saturated *[1 mark]* and further rainfall can't infiltrate it *[1 mark]*. This increases runoff into rivers, which increases discharge quickly *[1 mark]*.
   c)   E.g. if the rocks in an area are more impermeable, there is less infiltration and more runoff into the river channel *[1 mark]*, increasing river discharge and increasing the risk of flooding *[1 mark]*.
2 a) i)   20:00 on day 1 *[1 mark]*
    ii)

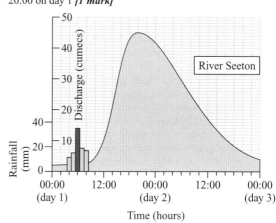

[1 mark]

    iii)   18 hours *[1 mark]*

Component 1: The Physical Environment

b) Any one from: e.g. the River Seeton is more likely to flood *[1 mark]* because it has a higher peak discharge, meaning that there is more water in the channel *[1 mark]*. / The River Seeton is more likely to flood *[1 mark]* because it has a shorter lag time, meaning that discharge increases more quickly *[1 mark]*.

c) Any two from: e.g. people can be killed or injured by floodwater *[1 mark]*. / Contamination by sewage can lead to a lack of clean drinking water *[1 mark]*. / People can be made homeless as their properties are flooded or damaged *[1 mark]*. / Important services like schools and hospitals may have to close *[1 mark]*.

You could also have mentioned that the flooding of electrical sub-stations can leave people without power, that transport links can be affected, or that businesses may be forced to shut down, leading to a loss of livelihoods.

d) E.g. floodwater contaminated with sewage and rubbish can pollute rivers and nearby areas *[1 mark]*, damaging wildlife habitats *[1 mark]*.

You could also have mentioned that farmland can be ruined by the deposition of silt and sediment after a flood, that floods causes huge changes to the river landscape, e.g. widening of the river channel, that the force of floodwater can uproot trees and plants, or that standing floodwater can cause trees and plants to die.

Pages 23-24: Human Activities in River Landscapes

1 a) i) Channelisation *[1 mark]*

ii) Channelisation may cause flooding or increased erosion at Fultow *[1 mark]* because flood water is carried there faster *[1 mark]*.

iii) Flood plain zoning reduces the risk of flooding because impermeable surfaces aren't created, e.g. buildings and roads *[1 mark]*. It also reduces the impact of flooding because there aren't any houses or roads to be damaged *[1 mark]*.

b) E.g. washlands are areas of flood plains that are deliberately allowed to flood during wet periods *[1 mark]*. The water stored in them reduces river discharge and the risk of flooding downstream *[1 mark]*.

c) E.g. eroded material is deposited in the reservoir and not along the river's natural course *[1 mark]*, which can prevent the formation of depositional landforms downstream *[1 mark]*.

2 a) Any one from: e.g. there are more houses and roads (urbanisation) *[1 mark]*. / There is less woodland (deforestation) *[1 mark]*. / There are more factories *[1 mark]*.

b) Any two from: e.g. urbanisation increases the amount of impermeable surfaces in the area, which increases the amount of surface runoff *[1 mark]*. This increases river discharge and velocity, which can lead to more erosion and transportation *[1 mark]*. / The development of industry can include dredging rivers to deepen the river channel *[1 mark]*. This increases river velocity, which can cause more erosion *[1 mark]*. / Air pollution from factories can make rainwater more acidic *[1 mark]*, which can result in more chemical weathering *[1 mark]*. / Deforestation reduces the interception of rainfall by plants and the infiltration of rain into the soil *[1 mark]*, which increases surface runoff and river discharge after storms, leading to more erosion *[1 mark]*.

c) Any one from: e.g. ploughing farmland exposes soil and allows it to be washed away into rivers when it rains *[1 mark]*. This means rivers have a bigger sediment load, which leads to more deposition downstream *[1 mark]*. / Irrigation can involve extracting water from rivers, which reduces river discharge *[1 mark]*. This can reduce erosion and transportation, and increase deposition *[1 mark]*.

d) This question is level marked. How to grade your answer:

Level 0: There is no relevant information. *[0 marks]*

Level 1: There is a basic description of some of the impacts of human activity on a named UK river landscape. *[1-3 marks]*

Level 2: There is a clear examination of some of the impacts of human activity on a named UK river landscape. *[4-6 marks]*

Level 3: There is a detailed examination of a range of impacts of human activity on a named UK river landscape. *[7-8 marks]*

You must refer to a named example in your answer. Here are some points your answer may include:

• A description of the different types of human activity occurring in the area, e.g. urbanisation, agriculture, industry and the construction of flood defences.

• An explanation of how each of these activities is affecting the landscape in the river basin.

• An examination of how the combination of different human activities is affecting river processes and the landscape.

• Your answer could refer to the Eden basin, where channel management, farming and deforestation are all occurring. Flood defences (such as flood walls in Carlisle and channel straightening in many areas) have altered the pattern of erosion and deposition along the river channel and prevented the formation of features such as meanders. Some farmers have drained moisture from the soil, making it more prone to erosion. This means there is more sediment entering the river channel, and there are higher rates of deposition downstream. Trees have been cleared from many upland parts of the basin, increasing runoff. This has meant that there is more water, with more erosive energy, entering the river channel.

Glaciated Upland Landscapes and Processes

Pages 25-26: Glacial Erosion and Landforms

1 a) B *[1 mark]*

An arête is a narrow, steep-sided ridge. Look at the really thin hill with tightly packed, parallel contours on either side. Its name, 'Striding Edge', is a clue too.

b) i) 3614 *[1 mark]*.

ii) Glacial troughs start off as V-shaped river valleys *[1 mark]*. Glaciers erode the sides and bottom of the valley, forming a U-shaped glacial trough *[1 mark]*.

c) 1.7 km (allow 1.6-1.8 km) *[1 mark]*

d) i) Corrie *[1 mark]*

You may also have called this feature a cwm or a cirque — these are correct too.

ii) A corrie begins as a hollow containing a small glacier *[1 mark]*. As the ice moves by rotational slip *[1 mark]*, it erodes the hollow into a steep-sided, armchair shape with a lip at the bottom end *[1 mark]*.

e) Helvellyn *[1 mark]*

2 a) i) D *[1 mark]*

ii) Hanging valleys are valleys formed by smaller tributary glaciers that flow into the main glacier *[1 mark]*. The glacial trough is eroded much more deeply by the larger glacier *[1 mark]*, so when the glaciers melt, the valleys of the tributary glaciers are left at a higher level *[1 mark]*.

b) E.g. plucking occurs when meltwater at the base, back or sides of a glacier freezes onto the rock *[1 mark]*. As the glacier moved forward it pulled pieces of rock off the mountain face, making the back wall steeper *[1 mark]*. Abrasion occurs when bits of rock stuck in the ice grind against the rock below the glacier, wearing it away *[1 mark]*. Abrasion wore away rock at the base of the glacier, making the base deeper and forming the hollow between X and Y (which is now a tarn) *[1 mark]*.

You may have also described how glaciers move in a circular motion (called rotational slip) as part of your answer. This erodes hollows in the landscape like the one shown in the photo.

c) An arête is formed when two glaciers flow in parallel valleys *[1 mark]*. The glaciers erode the sides of the valleys, forming a narrow, steep-sided ridge between them *[1 mark]*.

Page 27: Glacial Landforms and Processes

1 a) E.g. truncated spurs are formed when ridges sticking out into the main valley *[1 mark]* are eroded and cut off by a glacier *[1 mark]*.

CGP

GCSE Geography
For Edexcel A (Grade 9-1)

Exam Practice Answer Book

Contents

Component 1: The Physical Environment

Component 2: The Human Environment

Component 3: Geographical Investigations — Fieldwork and UK Challenges

Graph of world urban population on page 13 from Annual Urban Population at Mid-Year, by UN Population Division, © 2019 United Nations. Reprinted with the permission of the United Nations. https://esa.un.org/unpd/wup/DataQuery/

Published by CGP

ISBN: 978 1 78908 303 3

www.cgpbooks.co.uk
Printed by Elanders Ltd, Newcastle upon Tyne
Clipart from Corel®

Based on the classic CGP style created by Richard Parsons.

Component 1: The Physical Environment

Topic 1 — The Changing Landscapes of the UK

Pages 4-5: Rocks and the UK Physical Landscape

1 a)   C *[1 mark]*, E *[1 mark]*
  b) i) Any one from: e.g. sandstone *[1 mark]* / chalk *[1 mark]*
     ii) E.g. sedimentary rocks are formed when layers of sediment, such as sand *[1 mark]*, are compacted together *[1 mark]*.
  c) i) A rock formed when magma (molten rock) cools and hardens *[1 mark]*.
     ii) Any two from: e.g. igneous rocks are usually hard *[1 mark]*. / Igneous rocks contain crystals that form as the rock cools *[1 mark]*. / They are often impermeable *[1 mark]*.
     iii) Igneous rocks are generally found in the north and west of the UK *[1 mark]*. They are mostly found in Scotland and Northern Ireland *[1 mark]*.
2 a) i) Igneous *[1 mark]*
     ii) Granite is resistant to erosion, so softer rocks around the granite were eroded more quickly, leaving the granite above the rest of the landscape *[1 mark]*. Joints or weaker parts of the rock have been weathered, creating the deep cracks in the rock shown in Figure 2 *[1 mark]*.
  b)   E.g. they are usually relatively soft rocks (e.g. chalk and sandstone) *[1 mark]*.
  c)   E.g. ice eroded the landscape, carving out large U-shaped valleys *[1 mark]*. / As glaciers melted, they deposited thick layers of till/unsorted material on the landscapes *[1 mark]*.
  d)   E.g. in the past, the UK was much closer to a plate boundary than it is now *[1 mark]*. Active volcanoes forced magma to the surface, forming igneous rocks *[1 mark]*. The heat and pressure caused by plate collisions formed metamorphic rocks *[1 mark]*. This also caused rocks to be folded and uplifted, forming mountain ranges *[1 mark]*.

Page 6: Landscape Processes — Physical

1 a)   E.g. freeze-thaw weathering *[1 mark]*
  b)   E.g. as the rocks on the steep valley sides are broken up, there may be rockfalls *[1 mark]*, leading to the formation of scree slopes *[1 mark]*. / Slumping caused by the saturation of the soil *[1 mark]* may be making the valley sides less steep *[1 mark]*.
  c)   Any one from: e.g. a cold climate will increase the likelihood of freeze-thaw weathering *[1 mark]*, which will break down rocks on the valley sides *[1 mark]*. / A wetter climate will increase the number of streams and rivers *[1 mark]*, which will erode gullies in the valley sides *[1 mark]*.
2   E.g. the meandering river may have eroded the valley laterally, widening the valley floor *[1 mark]*. The wet climate in the UK may have led to flooding *[1 mark]*. The overflowing river may have deposited silt on the valley floor, forming a flood plain *[1 mark]*.

Page 7: Landscape Processes — Human

1 a)   Any one from: e.g. farm building labelled (Snarehill Farm) *[1 mark]* / land cleared of trees and not built on *[1 mark]*.
  b)   Any two from: e.g. people have built roads *[1 mark]*. / People have built houses *[1 mark]*. / Embankments have been built to make the road level *[1 mark]*.
  c)   E.g. areas of coniferous forest have been planted *[1 mark]*. These areas are often planted in straight rows, resulting in an unnatural landscape *[1 mark]*.
  d)   Any two from: e.g. warm/mild climate *[1 mark]* / flat land *[1 mark]* / good soils *[1 mark]*.
  e)   Conditions in upland areas are harsher than in lowland areas *[1 mark]*. Farming there tends to be sheep farming because they can cope with the steep slopes and colder weather *[1 mark]*.

Coastal Landscapes and Processes

Page 8: Coastal Weathering and Erosion

1 a)   Any two from: hydraulic action *[1 mark]* is when waves crash against rock and compress the air in the cracks. This puts pressure on the rock. Repeated compression widens the cracks and makes bits of rock break off *[1 mark]*. / Abrasion *[1 mark]* is when eroded particles in the water scrape and rub against rock, removing small pieces *[1 mark]*. / Solution *[1 mark]* is when slightly acidic sea water reacts chemically with rocks, dissolving them *[1 mark]*.
  b)   E.g. saltwater from the sea gets into cracks in the cliffs *[1 mark]*. When the water evaporates, salt crystals form *[1 mark]*. As the salt crystals form they expand, which puts pressure on the rock *[1 mark]*. Repeated evaporation and formation of salt crystals widens the cracks, causing the rock to break up *[1 mark]*.
  c)   Any one from: some rocks in the cliffs, such as chalk, could be affected by carbonation weathering *[1 mark]*, which is when carbonic acid in rainwater dissolves them *[1 mark]*. / Rocks in the cliffs could be broken up by freeze-thaw weathering *[1 mark]*. This is when cracks in rocks are widened by water in them expanding and contracting due to freezing and thawing *[1 mark]*. / Rocks in the cliffs could be broken down by biological weathering *[1 mark]*, which is when living things, e.g. plant roots, grow into cracks, pushing them apart *[1 mark]*.

Page 9: Coastal Transport and Deposition

1 a)   E.g. at 0 m, the beach was 5 m wider in 2010 than it was in 2018 *[1 mark]*. At 1000 m, the beach was 7-8 m narrower in 2010 than 2018 *[1 mark]*. The width of the beach varied by 5 m in 2010, but by much more in 2018 (17-18 m) *[1 mark]*.
  b)   E.g. the sediment was transported by longshore drift *[1 mark]*. The swash carries material up the beach, in the same direction as the prevailing wind *[1 mark]*. The backwash then carries material down the beach at right angles to the beach, back towards the sea *[1 mark]*. Over time, material zigzags along the coast, eroding the beach where material is transported away and building the beach where the material is deposited *[1 mark]*.
  c)   Traction *[1 mark]* and saltation *[1 mark]*.
  d)   E.g. there is a lot of erosion elsewhere on the coast, so there is a lot of material available *[1 mark]*. / This part of the coast is a low energy environment *[1 mark]*.
  e)   Constructive waves *[1 mark]*

Pages 10-12: Coastal Landforms

1 a)   Headland *[1 mark]* / Cliff *[1 mark]*
  b)   Waves eroded the foot of the cliff, which formed a wave-cut notch *[1 mark]*. The notch was enlarged as erosion continued *[1 mark]*. The rock above the wave-cut notch became unstable and collapsed *[1 mark]*.
  c) i) E.g. warmer temperatures in the summer can increase the rate of cliff retreat by increasing salt weathering *[1 mark]*, because seawater in cracks in cliffs evaporates more quickly *[1 mark]*.
     ii) Any one from: strong winds can increase the rate of cliff retreat *[1 mark]* because they create high energy, destructive waves, which increase erosion *[1 mark]*. / Intense rainfall can increase the rate of cliff retreat *[1 mark]* because the cliffs become saturated, making mass movement more likely *[1 mark]*. / Prevailing winds in the UK are mostly from the south-west *[1 mark]*, which means cliffs that are most exposed to these winds will retreat more quickly *[1 mark]*.
  d)   Your answer will depend on the coastal landscape you have chosen. E.g. the Dorset coastline is concordant to the west and discordant to the east *[1 mark]*. On the discordant stretch of coastline, the softer bands of sandstone and clay have been eroded to form bays, e.g. Swanage Bay *[1 mark]*, leaving the harder limestone and chalk exposed as headlands, e.g. the Foreland *[1 mark]*. On the concordant stretch of coastline, waves eroded a crack in the hard limestone until they broke through to the band of softer clay behind it, which was eroded into a small bay (Lulworth Cove) *[1 mark]*.

Component 1: The Physical Environment

2 a) Cave *[1 mark]*. It was formed when waves crashing into the headland enlarged cracks in the rock *[1 mark]* — mainly by hydraulic action and abrasion *[1 mark]*. Repeated erosion and enlargement of the cracks caused a cave to form *[1 mark]*.

b) One mark for arch correctly labelled.

c) The side of the headland was eroded by the sea to form a cave *[1 mark]*. Continued erosion deepened the cave until it broke through the headland and formed an arch *[1 mark]*.

3 E.g. over time, the waves will erode the landforms in this coastal area, e.g. by abrasion *[1 mark]*. The rock supporting the arch could be eroded further, causing the arch to collapse and form a stack *[1 mark]*. The cave may be eroded further to form an arch *[1 mark]*. The bay may be eroded further, forming a deeper bay *[1 mark]*.

You could also have mentioned that the rock could be broken down by weathering processes.

4 a) 991802 *[1 mark]*

b) 2.0 km (accept between 1.9 km and 2.1 km) *[1 mark]*

You'll have needed to use a ruler and the scale at the bottom of Figure 4 to work this out.

c) Longshore drift transported sand and shingle north east past a sharp bend in the coastline *[1 mark]* and deposited it in the sea, forming a spit *[1 mark]*.

d) The spit could continue to grow across the bay *[1 mark]*, creating a bar *[1 mark]*.

5 This question is level marked. How to grade your answer:

Level 0: There is no relevant information. *[0 marks]*

Level 1: There is a basic examination of how different physical processes have interacted in the formation of the coastline. *[1-3 marks]*

Level 2: There is a clear examination of how different physical processes have interacted in the formation of the coastline. *[4-6 marks]*

Level 3: There is a detailed examination of how different physical processes have interacted in the formation of the coastline. *[7-8 marks]*

Here are some points your answer may include:

- The coastline in Figure 5 features rocky headlands and bays with beaches.
- The south-west-facing part of the coastline in Figure 5 is discordant. Softer sedimentary rock has been eroded, e.g. by hydraulic action, to form the bays, leaving the harder igneous rock as headlands.
- The prevailing wind is from the south-west, which makes the southwesterly part of the coast vulnerable to erosion by waves and exposed to storms, and this is where the bays have been eroded into the cliffs.
- Some of the material that was eroded from the coast has been worn down by erosional processes (e.g. attrition) and deposited as sand or shingle on beaches.
- Beaches have developed in the bays because they are generally more sheltered, so waves there have less energy and are therefore more likely to deposit material than transport it away.

Page 13: Human Activity at the Coast

1 a) Any one from: e.g. it might mean that the cliffs erode quite quickly *[1 mark]* because the farmland is of low economic value so is unlikely to be protected *[1 mark]*. / It could cause the cliffs to become more unstable and easily eroded *[1 mark]* because the natural vegetation is removed by grazing, exposing the soil *[1 mark]*.

b) Any one from: e.g. urban areas might have more coastal defences than other areas to protect businesses and homes *[1 mark]*, which might reduce erosion *[1 mark]*. / Building on coastal lowlands can reduce the supply of sediment to beaches, making them narrower *[1 mark]*. This makes the coast more vulnerable to erosion *[1 mark]*.

2 a) 2.6 *[1 mark]*

The mean is the total of the values divided by the number of values. The total is 0 + 0 + 1 + 2 + 3 + 2 + 4 + 4 + 5 + 5 = 26. There are 10 years, so the mean is 26 ÷ 10 = 2.6.

b) Any one from: e.g. people may not be able to inhabit some low-lying coastal areas any more *[1 mark]* because they are permanently flooded or are flooded too often *[1 mark]*. / Coastal industries may be shut down *[1 mark]* because of damage to equipment and buildings *[1 mark]*. / Transport can be disrupted *[1 mark]* because of flood damage to roads and rail networks *[1 mark]*. / Flooding can damage tourism in coastal areas *[1 mark]* by putting people off visiting *[1 mark]*. / Agricultural land can be damaged by saltwater *[1 mark]* because it reduces soil fertility *[1 mark]*.

c) Your answer will depend on the coastal landscape you have chosen. E.g. on the Dorset coast, quarrying on the Isle of Portland has removed resistant limestone from the cliffs *[1 mark]*, which has left the softer rock underneath vulnerable to weathering and erosion *[1 mark]*.

Page 14: Coastal Defences

1 a) A *[1 mark]*

b) Beach nourishment creates wider beaches *[1 mark]* which slow the waves, giving greater protection from flooding and erosion *[1 mark]*.

c) E.g. taking material from the sea bed for beach nourishment can kill organisms like sponges and corals *[1 mark]*.
Beach nourishment is a very expensive defence that has to be repeated *[1 mark]*.

d) Cliffall is a town, so managed retreat would mean allowing homes and businesses to be lost to the sea *[1 mark]*. This would have large social and economic costs *[1 mark]*.

e) E.g. hard engineering strategies can reduce rates of coastal erosion *[1 mark]*. For example, a sea wall reflects waves back out to sea, protecting the coast from erosion by waves *[1 mark]*.

River Landscapes and Processes

Pages 15-16: River Processes

1 a) B *[1 mark]*

The source is the start of the river, where it is at its highest point.

b) A *[1 mark]*

Particles carried by the river bump into one another causing fragments to break off and their edges also get rounded off as they rub together. This process is called attrition.

c) Discharge increases along the course of a river *[1 mark]*, because more streams/tributaries join the main river *[1 mark]*.

d) Your answer will depend on the river you have chosen. E.g. the upper course of the River Eden flows over hard, resistant rocks *[1 mark]*, so the river channel is narrow and the valley has steep sides *[1 mark]*. The lower course flows through an area of sandstone, which is more easily eroded *[1 mark]*. This has allowed the river to erode laterally, forming a wide channel in a flat valley *[1 mark]*.

You could also have mentioned that the channel has a steep gradient in the upper course of the River Eden due to the resistant rock, whereas in the flatter landscape of the lower course it has a much gentler gradient.

e) E.g. when water in cracks in rock freezes, it expands, putting pressure on the rock *[1 mark]*. When the water thaws, it contracts, which releases the pressure on the rock *[1 mark]*. Repeated freezing and thawing widens the cracks and causes the rock to break up *[1 mark]*. This makes rockfalls more likely, changing the shape of the valley sides *[1 mark]*.

Component 1: The Physical Environment

b)   E.g. a freeze-thaw weathering could cause the rock to break into small blocks *[1 mark]*, which could fall down the slope in a rock fall *[1 mark]*.
You could also have written about soil creep, when rain causes the soil to become heavier and move downslope, and rock slides, which is when a large number of rocks shift as one mass.

2   a) i)   10 °C *[1 mark]*
The range is the difference between the highest and lowest values for daytime temperature. The highest daytime temperature is 12 °C and the lowest is 2 °C, so the range = 12 − 2 = 10 °C.
        ii)   6.5 °C *[1 mark]*
The mean daytime temperature for February is 2.5 °C and the mean night-time temperature is − 4 °C, so the difference is 2.5 − (−4) = 6.5 °C.

b)   E.g. diurnal variations during the winter months, e.g. February, mean that the temperature fluctuates from above freezing in the day to below freezing at night *[1 mark]*. This causes water in cracks in the rock to freeze and expand at night, putting pressure on the rock *[1 mark]*. The ice then thaws in the day, releasing the pressure *[1 mark]*. As this process is repeated, it can make bits of rock break off/shatter *[1 mark]*.
This process is known as freeze-thaw weathering.

Page 28: Glacial Transportation and Deposition

1   a)   C *[1 mark]*
Ground moraines are eroded material that is dragged along the base of a glacier and deposited across the valley floor as the ice melts.

b)   Any one from: the material can be frozen in the glacier *[1 mark]*. / The material can be carried on the surface of the glacier *[1 mark]*. / The material can be pushed in front of the glacier (bulldozing) *[1 mark]*.

c)   A terminal moraine formed at the snout of the glacier *[1 mark]*. Material was abraded and plucked from the valley floor and transported at the front of the glacier *[1 mark]*. When the ice retreated, the material was deposited as a semicircular mound *[1 mark]*.

2   a)
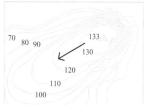
[1 mark]

b)   Crags are formed where a glacier erodes softer rock around an area of resistant rock *[1 mark]*, leaving the resistant rock as a steep hill *[1 mark]*. The tail is made from softer rock which is protected by the crag and is eroded by the glacier into a smooth slope *[1 mark]* or made by deposition when the glacier drops till after it passes over the crag *[1 mark]*.

Pages 29-30: Human Activities in Glaciated Landscapes

1   a)   Any two from: e.g. forestry *[1 mark]* / quarrying *[1 mark]* / generating wind energy *[1 mark]*

b)   E.g. building settlements increases the amount of ground covered with impermeable surfaces *[1 mark]*. This increases the amount of water that runs overland into rivers, instead of being stored in soil and plants, increasing the risk of flooding *[1 mark]*.

c)   E.g. livestock farming and forestry both prevent natural vegetation from growing *[1 mark]*. Sheep eat young trees before they grow and planting conifers can prevent other plants from growing as the conifers block out the sunlight *[1 mark]*. However, sheep grazing exposes soil to erosion, whereas the roots of trees in forestry plantations hold soil together *[1 mark]*.

d)   Advantage: e.g. having additional water storage can prevent shortages in the summer *[1 mark]*.
Disadvantage: e.g. habitats are destroyed when areas are flooded to create reservoirs *[1 mark]*.

2   a)   17.5 hectares *[1 mark]*

b)   E.g. there are plenty of activities for people to do, e.g. walking, rock climbing, cycling, canoeing *[1 mark]*. There is attractive scenery for people to visit, e.g. lakes and mountains *[1 mark]*.

c)   E.g. recreation and tourism require the development of infrastructure like roads, paths and buildings to cater for tourist activities *[1 mark]*.

d)   E.g. tourism provides income to the area *[1 mark]*, which that can be invested in conservation, e.g. replanting native woodland *[1 mark]*.

e)   Any two from: e.g. wind turbines can kill or injure birds *[1 mark]*. / Some people feel that structures like dams/wind turbines spoil the scenery, which can discourage tourists from visiting the area *[1 mark]*. / When dams for hydroelectric power generation are created, large areas are flooded, destroying habitats *[1 mark]*.

f)   This question is level marked. How to grade your answer:
        Level 0:   There is no relevant information. *[0 marks]*
        Level 1:   There is a basic description of human activities and how they have affected physical processes in the glaciated upland landscape. *[1-3 marks]*
        Level 2:   There is a clear examination of several different human activities and how they have affected physical processes in the glaciated upland landscape. There is a basic explanation of how these different impacts relate to one another. *[4-6 marks]*
        Level 3:   There is a detailed examination of several different human activities and how they have affected physical processes in the glaciated upland landscape. There is a clear explanation of how these different impacts relate to one another. *[7-8 marks]*
You must refer to a named example in your answer.
Here are some points your answer may include:
*   A brief description of the location of your chosen glaciated upland landscape.
*   The main human activities that the landscape has been used for.
*   The impact of each of these activities on the landscape and the physical processes at work within it.
*   E.g. you could talk about Snowdonia, and how sheep farming and mining for slate, copper and gold have removed natural vegetation. This has affected erosional processes in the area — vegetation holds soil and rock together, so a lack of vegetation means the soil is more vulnerable to erosion and mass movement. The area is very popular with tourists, receiving about 4 million visitors every year. Tourism has led to the trampling of vegetation around footpaths and verges, especially around Snowdon, which can increase rates of erosion. Vegetation has also been cleared to build infrastructure to accommodate visitors. This can make the soil more vulnerable to erosion and increase surface run-off, which can lead to a greater risk of flooding.

Topic 2 — Weather Hazards and Climate Change

Page 31: Global Atmospheric Circulation & Heat Transfer

1   a)   C *[1 mark]*
b)   0° (the equator) *[1 mark]*
c) i)   The Sun heats the Earth at the equator, causing air to warm up and rise *[1 mark]*. As the air rises it cools and moves away from the equator *[1 mark]*. The cool air sinks and some is drawn towards the poles as surface winds *[1 mark]*.
    ii)   Water at the poles freezes and releases salt into the water around it, making the water denser *[1 mark]*. The dense water sinks and warmer water flows in at the surface, creating a current *[1 mark]*.

Component 1: The Physical Environment

Page 32: Natural Climate Change

1 a) Temperature has changed/fluctuated in cycles of approximately 100 000 years *[1 mark]*. The temperature difference ranges between -9 °C and +3 °C from the present day *[1 mark]*.

b) Ice sheets are made up of layers of ice, with one new layer formed each year *[1 mark]*. By analysing the gases trapped in the layers of ice, scientists can tell what the temperature was in each year *[1 mark]*.

c) E.g. changes in the Earth's orbit affect the amount of solar radiation/energy that the Earth receives *[1 mark]*. Periods of warming could have been caused by the Earth receiving more solar energy as it came closer to the Sun *[1 mark]*. / The Sun's output of energy changes in short cycles of about 11 years *[1 mark]*, so periods of cooling could have been caused by periods of reduced solar output *[1 mark]*.

You could also have written about material released from volcanic eruptions reflecting the Sun's rays back out to space, meaning that less energy reached the Earth.

d) Any one from: e.g. diary entries *[1 mark]* often have details of harvest dates and the number of days of snow or rain *[1 mark]*. / Paintings *[1 mark]* provide a visual record of what the weather was like in the past *[1 mark]*. / Tree rings *[1 mark]* because their width shows how warm or cold the climate was at different times *[1 mark]*. / Pollen records *[1 mark]* show which plant species were alive in the past, allowing scientists to work out what the climate was like by looking at the conditions that those plants live in now *[1 mark]*.

Page 33: Climate Change — Human Activity

1 a) Burning coal releases carbon dioxide into the atmosphere, so coal-fired power plants increase the concentration of greenhouse gases in the atmosphere *[1 mark]*. Greenhouse gases absorb outgoing heat, so less is lost to space — this is called the greenhouse effect *[1 mark]*. Increasing the amount of greenhouse gas in the atmosphere enhances the greenhouse effect, trapping more heat and causing the planet to warm up *[1 mark]*.

b) Any one from: e.g. farming of livestock produces a lot of methane *[1 mark]*, which is a greenhouse gas that contributes to climate change *[1 mark]*. / Cement contains limestone, which contains carbon *[1 mark]*. Producing cement releases this carbon as CO_2, increasing the greenhouse effect and contributing to climate change *[1 mark]*. / Most forms of transport burn fossil fuels *[1 mark]*. Fossil fuels release greenhouse gases when they're burned *[1 mark]*.

You could also have written about rice-growing releasing lots of methane, burning trees to clear land releasing lots of CO_2 or industrial waste releasing methane as it decays in landfill.

2 a) i) The overall decrease in rainfall from 2003 to 2018 corresponds to a decrease in maize yield *[1 mark]*. This suggests that climate change may be related to decreases in crop yields *[1 mark]*.

ii) Any one from: e.g. less food being grown could lead to malnutrition, ill health and death from starvation *[1 mark]*. / People may migrate to other areas as food becomes scarce *[1 mark]*.

b) Any one from: e.g. climate change can lead to glacier retreat, which causes rivers to dry up and habitats to be lost *[1 mark]*. / Climate change could cause sea level rise, which would destroy coastal habitats *[1 mark]*.

Page 34: UK Climate

1 a) 20 °C *[1 mark]*

b)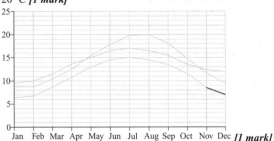
[1 mark]

c) Location C *[1 mark]*, because it has lower temperatures through the year *[1 mark]*.

d) E.g. the Medieval Warm Period was a period of warmer climate from around 900-1300 *[1 mark]*.

2 a) i) B *[1 mark]*

ii) E.g. prevailing winds in the UK come from the south west *[1 mark]*. These winds brings moist air from the Atlantic, which hit the west coast of the UK first, so it tends to have higher rainfall than the east *[1 mark]*.

You could also have talked about how the north and west of the UK are affected by maritime air masses, which are associated with higher rainfall.

b) E.g. the UK is surrounded by the sea, which stores heat better than land *[1 mark]* and so keeps the UK warmer in winter than countries in continental Europe, which may be surrounded by land/have smaller coastlines *[1 mark]*.

You could also have talked about the North Atlantic Drift, which brings warm water from the Caribbean to the west coast of the UK, making the west coast of the UK warmer than other countries at similar latitudes, like Germany.

Pages 35-37: Tropical Cyclones

1 a) All tropical cyclones form near the equator *[1 mark]*, then move westwards and away from the equator *[1 mark]*.

b) In the northern hemisphere, the majority of cyclones occur in late summer and autumn *[1 mark]*, because this is when sea temperatures are highest *[1 mark]*.

c) Tropical cyclones form when the sea temperature is 27 °C or higher *[1 mark]* and wind shear between higher and lower parts of the atmosphere is low *[1 mark]*. The warm sea temperatures cause air to rise, creating an area of low pressure *[1 mark]*. The low pressure increases surface winds, which get stronger due to energy from the warm water and form a cyclone *[1 mark]*.

d) Any two from: e.g. tropical cyclones have a circular shape *[1 mark]*. / They are hundreds of kilometres wide *[1 mark]*. / Tropical cyclones have an eye at their centre, which is up to 50 km across *[1 mark]*. / In the eye of the tropical cyclone, pressure is low and winds are light *[1 mark]*. / There is an eyewall that surrounds the eye *[1 mark]*. / In the eyewall there are very strong winds, torrential rain and a low temperature *[1 mark]*.

e) A *[1 mark]*

2 a) Windspeed *[1 mark]*

b) E.g. the cyclone lost energy as it moved over cooler water away from the equator *[1 mark]*.

c) Any two from: e.g. intense rainfall *[1 mark]* / storm surges *[1 mark]* / coastal flooding *[1 mark]* / landslides *[1 mark]*

3 a) E.g. high winds and flooding can damage or destroy property such as cars and houses *[1 mark]*. Tropical cyclones can damage infrastructure such as roads and electricity supplies *[1 mark]*.

b) Your answer will vary depending on the example you have chosen. E.g. in Myanmar, Cyclone Nargis destroyed 38 000 hectares of mangrove forests *[1 mark]*, which reduced the amount of habitats available for birds and other wildlife *[1 mark]*. Cyclone Nargis also caused the salination of soils *[1 mark]*, which damaged plants growing in affected areas *[1 mark]*.

Component 1: The Physical Environment

4 a) i) 6 billion ÷ 2 billion = 3, so the ratio is 3:1 *[1 mark]*

 ii) E.g. Tropical Cyclone B happened in an emerging country, where some buildings may be of a lower quality than in the developed country affected by Tropical Cyclone A *[1 mark]*. This means the buildings would be less able to withstand the strong winds and floods caused by a tropical cyclone *[1 mark]*.

 b) The cost of damage caused by a tropical cyclone is often higher in developed countries than emerging or developing countries *[1 mark]*. This is because e.g. developed countries have more advanced infrastructure and industry *[1 mark]*, which means that damage caused by tropical cyclones is likely to be more expensive to repair *[1 mark]*.

 c) Your answer will vary depending on the example you have chosen. E.g. in the USA, after Hurricane Katrina, local and international charities provided millions of hot meals *[1 mark]*. An amateur radio network volunteered to provide emergency communications systems in places where communications infrastructure was destroyed *[1 mark]*.

 d) This question is level marked. How to grade your answer:

 Level 0: There is no relevant information. *[0 marks]*

 Level 1: There are a few points about how individuals and governments respond to tropical cyclones. *[1-3 marks]*

 Level 2: There is a clear assessment of how individuals and governments respond to tropical cyclones, and some attempt is made to relate the responses to the country's level of development. *[4-6 marks]*

 Level 3: There is a detailed assessment of how individuals and governments respond to tropical cyclones, and a clear explanation of how the responses are affected by the country's level of development. *[7-8 marks]*

 Your answer must refer to named examples.

 Here are some points your answer may include:

 • A brief description of the level of development in your chosen countries.
 • A brief description of a tropical cyclone that has affected each of your chosen countries.
 • The individual and government responses to the cyclones in each country, e.g. preparation and emergency relief.
 • An assessment of the differences between the responses in each country, and how they relate to the country's level of development.
 • E.g. you could refer to the USA and responses to Hurricane Katrina. The USA is a developed country with the resources to forecast and prepare for cyclones, so individuals had plenty of warning about Hurricane Katrina and 70-80% of the residents in New Orleans were evacuated before the cyclone arrived. The government played a major role in the response to the cyclone, e.g. the US government provided $16 billion towards rebuilding people's houses and repairing infrastructure, and some individuals also volunteered to help rebuild their neighbourhoods.
 • E.g. you could refer to Myanmar and responses to Cyclone Nargis. Myanmar is a developing country, so many individuals lacked the resources to prepare for and respond to the climate. The warnings issued on the TV and radio did not reach many poorer people in rural areas and so did not know what to do or where to evacuate to. Many individuals had to recover and rebuild their homes without support, because the government did not have enough resources to help them and initially prevented international organisations from providing assistance.

Pages 38-39: Drought

1 a) i) 25 mm *[1 mark]*

 ii) There is very little rainfall *[1 mark]*, e.g. Figure 1 shows that the average rainfall peaks at about 25 mm a month but can be as low as about 5 mm a month *[1 mark]*.

 b) E.g. the rainfall in 2018 was much lower than the average for several months *[1 mark]*, which is likely to have caused a severe shortage of water, leading to a drought *[1 mark]*. The higher temperatures in 2018 might have increased rates of evaporation from surface stores of water *[1 mark]*, which reduced the amount of water available for people to use *[1 mark]*.

 c) Any two from: e.g. the depletion of water supplies can lead to lower levels in water bodies *[1 mark]*. This can cause contamination of water supplies as there is less dilution of waste materials like sewage *[1 mark]*. / A lack of water can damage crops and livestock, leading to food shortages *[1 mark]*. This can cause hunger and malnutrition *[1 mark]*. / Vegetation can become very dry, making wildfires more likely *[1 mark]*. Wildfires can damage ecosystems and settlements *[1 mark]*.

2 a) There are large areas affected by droughts of medium to high severity between 20° and 30° S, e.g. in Australia, southern Africa and the west coast of South America *[1 mark]* and between 20° and 30° N, e.g. north Africa and the Middle East *[1 mark]*. There are smaller areas of medium to high drought severity in areas of the far north, e.g. in North America and north east Asia *[1 mark]*.

 b) Many of the areas which experience droughts of medium to high severity are found in a belt of high pressure (formed when the Hadley cell meets the Ferrel cell) *[1 mark]*. This high pressure belt is caused by warm air from the equator cooling and sinking at around 30° north and south of the equator *[1 mark]*. The high pressure creates clear, dry and hot weather conditions, so many areas have little rainfall and are more vulnerable to drought *[1 mark]*.

3 a) Your answer will vary depending on the example you have chosen. E.g. in Australia, the government responded to the Millennium Drought by introducing water conservation measures such as reducing the allocation of water to each household *[1 mark]*. The government also provided income support to 23 000 rural families and 1500 small businesses *[1 mark]*.

 b) This question is level marked. There are 4 extra marks available for spelling, punctuation and grammar.

 How to grade your answer:

 Level 0: There is no relevant information. *[0 marks]*

 Level 1: There are a few points about the impacts of drought on developed and developing or emerging countries. *[1-3 marks]*

 Level 2: There is a clear assessment of how the impacts of drought vary between developed and developing or emerging countries. *[4-6 marks]*

 Level 3: There is a detailed assessment of how the impacts of drought vary between developed and developing or emerging countries, and a consideration of how development affects responses to drought. *[7-8 marks]*

 Make sure your spelling, punctuation and grammar are consistently correct, that your meaning is clear and that you use a range of geographical terms correctly *[0-4 marks]*.

 Your answer must refer to named examples.

 Here are some points your answer may include:

 • A brief description of the level of development in your chosen countries.
 • A brief description of a drought that has affected each of your chosen countries.
 • The impacts of the drought on ecosystems and people in each country.
 • An assessment of the differences in the severity of these impacts, and how it relates to the country's level of development.

Component 1: The Physical Environment

- E.g. you could refer to Australia and the Millennium Drought. The impacts of the drought included major losses in farming, including the loss of livestock and a decline in crop yields. This led to an increase in food prices, a drop in farmers' incomes, and unemployment among people working in farming. However, because Australia is a developed country, it was able to import food from elsewhere to prevent food shortages, and could provide income support to affected people. This helped reduce the impacts of the drought in the long term.

- E.g. you could refer to Ethiopia and the 2016 drought. The drought had big impacts on farming, with crop losses of 50-90% in some areas, and many farmers lost livestock. Ethiopia is a developing country, so for poorer people these losses led to food shortages and malnutrition. The government was able to help people in the short term, providing them with food and money through the Productive Safety Net Program, but lacks the resources to help people rebuild their livelihoods, so people are still suffering the consequences of the drought.

Topic 3 — Ecosystems, Biodiversity and Management

Pages 40-42: Global Ecosystems

1 a) Desert *[1 mark]*
   b) Tropical forests are found around the equator *[1 mark]*, in areas such as central America/north east South America/central Africa/south east Asia *[1 mark]*.
   c) Tundra environments are very cold with temperatures usually less than 10 °C *[1 mark]*. Precipitation is low — usually less than 250 mm per year *[1 mark]*.
   d) E.g. the organisms in different ecosystems are adapted to different climates, so each ecosystem only occurs in regions with a specific climate *[1 mark]*. For example, the climate around the equator is hot and wet and stays the same throughout the year, so tropical forests grow there *[1 mark]*. Areas around 23.5° north and south of the equator, such as North Africa, have very low rainfall, so desert ecosystems occur in dry conditions there *[1 mark]*.

2 a) July *[1 mark]*
   b) Temperate forest *[1 mark]*
   c) Temperate forests have lots of broad-leaved trees (e.g. oak) *[1 mark]*. There are also lots of shrubs and undergrowth (e.g. brambles) *[1 mark]*.

3 a) C *[1 mark]*
   b) Grasslands consist mostly of grass and small plants *[1 mark]*. There may be a few scattered trees, e.g. acacia *[1 mark]*.

4 a) Any one from: e.g. black bears *[1 mark]* / wolves *[1 mark]* / elk *[1 mark]* / eagles *[1 mark]*
   b) E.g. boreal forests are found in high latitudes *[1 mark]*.
   c) E.g. areas at higher altitudes tend to have colder climates and thinner soils than lower altitudes *[1 mark]*. Boreal forests are adapted to these conditions in the regions in which they are found *[1 mark]*.

5 a) E.g. tropical grasslands have thinner soils *[1 mark]* and fewer nutrients than temperate grasslands *[1 mark]*.
   b) E.g. the acidity, drainage, depth and nutrient content of the soil in an area affects what kinds of plants can grow there, which affects which ecosystem forms *[1 mark]*. For example, deep, nutrient-rich soils can support many plants, allowing biodiverse ecosystems such as temperate grasslands to form *[1 mark]*. In areas that only have a thin layer of soil containing organic matter, the lack of nutrients means that the soil can't support many plants, so desert ecosystems are found there *[1 mark]*.

Page 43: Humans and the Biosphere

1 a) E.g. plants with medicinal properties are used to cure illnesses *[1 mark]*.

   b) Mineral resources like gold and iron are needed for building and to make goods like electrical appliances *[1 mark]*. Demand for these is growing as the world's population increases, so more mining is happening to keep up with demand *[1 mark]*.

2 a) $\dfrac{4.04 - 5.42}{5.42} \times 100$

   = –25% (to nearest whole number) *[1 mark]*
   b) $\dfrac{4.89}{19} \times 100$

   = 26% (to nearest whole number) *[1 mark]*
   c) E.g. more trees are cut down to provide more fuel *[1 mark]* and to clear land so that more power stations can be built, e.g. HEP stations *[1 mark]*.

Pages 44-45: UK Ecosystems

1 a) Moorlands *[1 mark]*
   b) B *[1 mark]*
Woodlands used to cover most of the UK, but they are now mostly restricted to small areas throughout the UK's lowlands. There are also some larger areas of woodland in upland areas, e.g. Kielder Forest, and lowland areas, e.g the Forest of Dean.
   c) Any two from: e.g. heaths have poor soils *[1 mark]*. / Heaths have few trees *[1 mark]*. / The main plants are heather, gorse and grasses *[1 mark]*.

2 a) (Mixed) woodland *[1 mark]*
   b) South west *[1 mark]*
   c) E.g. Arnaby Marsh is a wetland, so the soils there are probably often waterlogged *[1 mark]*. The vegetation would be restricted to plants which can grow in these conditions, such as reeds and mosses *[1 mark]*.

3 a) Any two from: e.g. people use coastal areas for recreational activities such as watersports *[1 mark]*. / Tourism in coastal areas provides jobs *[1 mark]*. / Oil and gas for fuel are extracted from under the seabed using deep sea platforms *[1 mark]*. / Marine areas are used to generate renewable energy such as tidal, wave and wind energy *[1 mark]*.
   b) E.g. the amount of fish landings in the UK decreased considerably (by more than half) between 1938 and 2017 *[1 mark]*. The rate of decrease has not been even, e.g. fish landings have been declining more slowly since 1998 *[1 mark]*, and fish landings increased between 1938 and 1948 and between 1960 and 1970 *[1 mark]*.
   c) E.g. demand for fish in the UK is greater than the supply of wild fish, so fish populations have declined *[1 mark]*. This means that there are fewer fish available to catch, causing a decline in fish landings *[1 mark]*.
   d) Any two from: e.g. humans produce lots of plastic waste *[1 mark]*. The plastic gets eaten by marine animals and collects in their bodies, potentially killing them *[1 mark]*. / Excess fertilisers on farmland can run into estuaries *[1 mark]*. Fertilisers can cause algae to grow very quickly (eutrophication), restricting the supply of oxygen and light to the seabed and harming/killing organisms living in seabed habitats *[1 mark]*. / Humans clear/dredge material from the sea floor to create shipping routes *[1 mark]*. This damages seabed plants and reduces the supply of food to marine organisms *[1 mark]*.
You could also mention how fishing with trawl nets and building marine infrastructure can damage seabed habitats such as coral reefs, harming the organisms which live there.

Pages 46-47: Tropical Rainforests

1 a) E.g. many trees are very tall *[1 mark]*. / The vegetation cover is dense *[1 mark]*.
   b) The climate is the same all year round / there are no definite seasons *[1 mark]*. It's hot (the temperature is generally between 20-28 °C and only varies by a few degrees over the year) *[1 mark]*. Rainfall is very high (around 2000 mm per year) and it rains every day *[1 mark]*.

Component 1: The Physical Environment

c)   B *[1 mark]*

Soils in tropical rainforests are not very fertile because the nutrients are washed away by heavy rain. Plants get nutrients from a layer of decaying fallen leaves on the soil surface — this layer is thin because the leaves decay quickly in the warm, moist climate.

2   E.g. a decrease in the number of banana trees could reduce the number of insects in the rainforest, as insects feed on banana trees *[1 mark]*. This could lead to an decrease in the number of bats, as there will be fewer insects for them to eat *[1 mark]*.

3 a)   Any two from: e.g. the trees are very tall *[1 mark]* so that they can break through the canopy layer to reach the sunlight *[1 mark]*. / The trees have buttress roots above the ground *[1 mark]*, which allow them to get nutrients from the rich layer on the soil surface *[1 mark]*. / They only have leaves at the top *[1 mark]*, where there's most light *[1 mark]*. / Plants have waxy leaves with pointed tips *[1 mark]* which channel the water to a point so it runs off and the weight of it doesn't damage the plants *[1 mark]*.

   b)   Any two from: e.g. some animals are camouflaged *[1 mark]*, so they can hide from predators *[1 mark]*. / They may have strong limbs *[1 mark]* so that they can spend all day climbing and leaping from tree to tree *[1 mark]*. / Some birds have short, pointy wings *[1 mark]* so that they can easily manoeuvre between the dense tangle of branches in the trees *[1 mark]*. / Some birds have beaks which are specially adapted to their diet *[1 mark]*, for example macaws have short strong beaks which allow them to break open nuts *[1 mark]*.

4 a)   E.g. so that they can get more light *[1 mark]*. / So they are more likely to be pollinated by animals living in the canopy *[1 mark]*. / So their seeds can be dispersed by wind *[1 mark]*. / So they can get more water from rainfall *[1 mark]*.

   b)   Any three from: e.g. they are dependent on the climate having frequent rainfall for water *[1 mark]*. / They are dependent on their host plant to allow them to grow high enough to get the light they need *[1 mark]*. / They are dependent on dust/compost collecting on the branches of their host to provide the nutrients they need *[1 mark]*. / They may be dependent on animals for pollination *[1 mark]*. / They may be dependent on the wind to disperse their seeds *[1 mark]*.

Page 48: Tropical Rainforests — Nutrients & Biodiversity

1 a)   A *[1 mark]*
   b)   (Leaf) litter *[1 mark]*
   c)   Biomass *[1 mark]*
   d)   The dead organic litter is broken down by fungi and bacteria *[1 mark]*. The nutrients are soluble and soak into the soil *[1 mark]*.

2 a)   Biodiversity is the variety of organisms living in a particular area *[1 mark]*.

   b)   Any one from: e.g. rainforests have existed with a fairly stable climate for tens of millions of years *[1 mark]*, which has allowed plants and animals to evolve to form new species *[1 mark]*. / The stratified structure of vegetation in rainforests provides many different habitats *[1 mark]*, which means that plants and animals can become specialised and lots of different species can develop *[1 mark]*. / Rainforests are very stable ecosystems *[1 mark]* which means that plants and animals don't have to adapt to changing conditions and can specialise *[1 mark]*.

Page 49: Tropical Rainforests — Human Uses and Impacts

1 a)   E.g. the area of deforested land increased between 1966 and 2016 *[1 mark]*. The rate of deforestation was slow at first, but increased rapidly after 1996 *[1 mark]*.

   b)   Any two from: e.g. to extract timber *[1 mark]*. / To clear land for commercial farming *[1 mark]*. / To clear land for new or expanding settlements *[1 mark]*. / To provide fuel for cooking or to make charcoal for a growing population *[1 mark]*.

c)   E.g. tropical rainforests provide lots of goods and services *[1 mark]*. Tropical rainforests are a source of plants used in medicines and to produce important food crops like coffee and chocolate *[1 mark]*. Hardwoods, e.g. mahogany, are widely used for furniture and building *[1 mark]*. Tropical rainforests also provide places for tourism, study and recreation *[1 mark]*.

d)   Any two from: e.g. in some areas, climate change is causing temperature to increase and rainfall decrease *[1 mark]*. Plants and animals adapted to moist conditions may die due to drier weather *[1 mark]*. / Increased frequency of drought can lead to more forest fires *[1 mark]*, which can destroy large areas of forest, changing the structure of tropical rainforests *[1 mark]*. / Climate change may reduce the productivity of rainforests *[1 mark]*, meaning that they won't be able to support as many specialised plants and animals *[1 mark]*. / Leaf litter decomposes more slowly in drier conditions *[1 mark]*, so there may be fewer nutrients available to plants *[1 mark]*.

Page 50: Tropical Rainforests — Sustainable Management

1 a)   2250 tourists *[1 mark]*
   b)

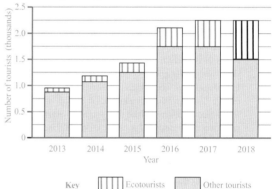

Key | | | | Ecotourists | | Other tourists
[1 mark]

   c)   The number of ecotourists has increased *[1 mark]* from about 100 in 2013 to 750 in 2018 *[1 mark]*.
   d)   E.g. people may be more aware of the threats to tropical rainforests and the need to conserve them *[1 mark]*. They may want to decrease their own impact on the rainforest, so they choose to travel as ecotourists *[1 mark]*.
   e)   D *[1 mark]*
   f)   This question is level marked. There are 4 extra marks available for spelling, punctuation and grammar.
        How to grade your answer:
        Level 0:   There is no relevant information. *[0 marks]*
        Level 1:   There is a basic description of the impacts of political and economic factors on the sustainable management of a tropical rainforest in a named location. *[1-3 marks]*
        Level 2:   There is a clear description and some assessment of the impacts of political and economic factors on the sustainable management of a tropical rainforest in a named location. *[4-6 marks]*
        Level 3:   There is a detailed description and assessment of the impacts of political and economic factors on the sustainable management of a tropical rainforest in a named location. *[7-8 marks]*
        Make sure your spelling, punctuation and grammar are consistently correct, that your meaning is clear and that you use a range of geographical terms correctly *[0-4 marks]*.
        Your answer must refer to a named example.
        Here are some points your answer may include:
        • A brief description of the tropical rainforest in your named location.
        • How political factors, e.g. governance, have contributed to the sustainable management of tropical rainforest in that location. E.g. you could talk about the Amazon rainforest and how national and international law has been used to restrict exploitation of parts of the rainforest.

Component 1: The Physical Environment

- How economic factors, e.g. commodity value and ecotourism, have contributed to the sustainable management of tropical rainforest in that location. E.g. you could talk about the Amazon rainforest and strategies that have increased the value of sustainably produced timber, such as Forest Stewardship Council® certification.
- Which factor has contributed most in the sustainable management of tropical rainforest in that location.

Pages 51-52: Deciduous Woodlands

1 a) E.g. leaves fall from the trees in the autumn and decompose in the mild, wet climate *[1 mark]*. This forms a layer of humus/ organic matter *[1 mark]* which is mixed into material from weathered bedrock to form a fertile soil called brown earth *[1 mark]*.

b) Any two from: e.g. deciduous woodlands are dominated by deciduous trees which lose their leaves in the autumn *[1 mark]*. / The vegetation in deciduous woodlands is stratified in four main layers *[1 mark]*. / Small mammals such as squirrels and dormice live in the trees *[1 mark]*. / Large mammals such as foxes live in burrows in the ground under the trees *[1 mark]*. / People get goods from woodlands, e.g. timber *[1 mark]*.

c) Deciduous woodlands have a temperate climate, so there are no extremes of temperature or rainfall *[1 mark]*. They have distinct seasons, with warm summers and cool winters *[1 mark]*. Rainfall is fairly high (about 1000 mm a year) and it rains all year round *[1 mark]*.

d) E.g. deciduous woodlands are interdependent ecosystems, so deforestation would have knock-on effects on both biotic and abiotic components of the ecosystem *[1 mark]*. The loss of trees would remove habitats for wildlife *[1 mark]* and reduce the amount of leaf fall, leading to a loss of soil fertility *[1 mark]*. A decline in soil fertility and the loss of wildlife that disperse seeds could make it harder for new plants/trees to get established and for the forest to recover *[1 mark]*.

2 a) A *[1 mark]*

b) E.g. trees lose water through openings in the surfaces of the leaves *[1 mark]*, so deciduous trees withdraw food and nutrients from their leaves in the autumn, causing the leaves to fall off the tree *[1 mark]*.

c) E.g. hibernation reduces animals' need for food *[1 mark]* and protects them from the cold *[1 mark]*.

d) E.g. some birds migrate during the winter *[1 mark]*, travelling to warmer climates nearer the equator where they can find food more easily *[1 mark]*. Some animals store food in the autumn when it is easily available *[1 mark]* and use these stores in the winter when there is less food available *[1 mark]*.

Page 53: Deciduous Woodlands — Nutrients & Biodiversity

1 a) E.g. lots of nutrients are transferred from the litter store through decomposition *[1 mark]*. The uptake of nutrients from the soil by plants is quite low because plants are only growing for part of the year *[1 mark]*.

b) E.g. litter decomposes more slowly in deciduous woodlands because the climate is cooler *[1 mark]*. Fewer nutrients are transferred through runoff and leaching because rainfall is lower in deciduous woodlands *[1 mark]*.

c) E.g. trees in deciduous woodlands shed their leaves in the autumn *[1 mark]*, so the litter store will be largest in autumn and winter and smallest in spring and summer *[1 mark]*.

d) Any two from: e.g. deciduous woodlands have a temperate climate with no extremes of temperature or rainfall *[1 mark]*, so a fairly large number of different plants and animals can survive there *[1 mark]*. / The different plant layers in deciduous woodlands *[1 mark]* provide several different habitats for plants and animals *[1 mark]*. / Many deciduous woodlands have experienced a lot of disturbance by human activities *[1 mark]*, which has prevented the vegetation from becoming established enough to support high biodiversity *[1 mark]*.

Page 54: Deciduous Woodlands — Human Uses and Impacts

1 a) Any one from: e.g. fuel *[1 mark]* / conservation *[1 mark]* / recreational activities e.g. mountain-biking, hiking and horse-riding *[1 mark]*

b) E.g. population growth and urbanisation *[1 mark]* are increasing demand for timber for use in construction *[1 mark]*.

2 a) $(10.20 - 9.25) \div 9.25 = 0.1027...$
$0.1027... \times 100 = 10.27\%$ (accept 10.3%) *[1 mark]*

b) E.g. higher temperatures in the winter could encourage animals to come out of hibernation too early *[1 mark]*, before there are enough sources of food for them to be able to survive *[1 mark]*.

c) Any one from: e.g. there could be more droughts, which means that trees might not have enough water *[1 mark]*. This could cause trees to grow more slowly or die *[1 mark]*. / There could be more storms, which could cause trees to be knocked down by strong winds *[1 mark]*, reducing the number of habitats available for wildlife *[1 mark]*. / Higher temperatures could allow insects which damage trees to increase in number *[1 mark]*, e.g. by allowing invasive species from warmer climates to move into deciduous woodlands *[1 mark]*.

Page 55: Deciduous Woodlands — Sustainable Management

1 a) i) E.g. building paths encourages people to take particular routes through the woodland *[1 mark]*, which keeps people away from easily damaged habitats *[1 mark]*.

ii) Any one from: e.g. building fences *[1 mark]* / installing cattle grids *[1 mark]* / putting up information signs *[1 mark]*.

b) Any two from: e.g. people learn about how they can look after the woodland *[1 mark]*. / People understand why the woodland is worth managing sustainably *[1 mark]*. / People learn about how the woodland is threatened *[1 mark]*. / People are encouraged to volunteer to help manage the forest *[1 mark]*.

c) Any one from: e.g. the high population could mean that lots of people use the New Forest for recreation *[1 mark]*, which could damage plants and disturb wildlife in the woodland *[1 mark]*. / There may be lots of people travelling/commuting through parts of the woodland *[1 mark]*, so management of wildlife, e.g. deer, is needed to help to avoid road traffic collisions *[1 mark]*.

d) This question is level marked. There are 4 extra marks available for spelling, punctuation and grammar.
How to grade your answer:
Level 0: There is no relevant information. *[0 marks]*
Level 1: There is a basic description of different approaches to the sustainable use and management of a deciduous woodland in a named region. *[1-3 marks]*
Level 2: There is a clear description of different approaches to the sustainable use and management of a deciduous woodland in a named region. There is a basic assessment of the effectiveness of these approaches. *[4-6 marks]*
Level 3: There is a detailed description of different approaches to the sustainable use and management of a deciduous woodland in a named region. There is a clear assessment of the effectiveness of these approaches. *[7-8 marks]*
Make sure your spelling, punctuation and grammar are consistently correct, that your meaning is clear and that you use a range of geographical terms correctly *[0-4 marks]*.
Your answer must refer to a named example.
Here are some points your answer may include:
- A brief description of the deciduous woodland in your named region, including the different ways that people use the woodland, e.g. timber and recreation.
- Who the stakeholders are and who is responsible for managing the woodland, e.g. governments, organisations, communities or individuals.

Component 2: The Human Environment

- Different approaches that stakeholders have taken to try to use and manage the deciduous woodland sustainably, e.g. conservation, recreation, education or sustainable forestry.
- The impacts of these approaches on the deciduous woodland, and the relative importance of their contribution to the sustainable management of the deciduous woodland.
- Your answer may have referred to the Forest of Dean, and how different stakeholders are carrying out different approaches to sustainable management, e.g. local and national organisations are running outreach and education activities, while the Forestry Commission is managing recreation by building trails and managing wildlife by carrying out a cull of wild boar. The combination of these different approaches is helping to manage the forest more sustainably, but can also lead to conflicts, e.g. over the management of wild boar.

Topic 4 — Changing Cities

Pages 56-57: Urbanisation

1 a)

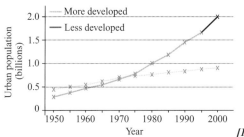

[1 mark]

b) $\dfrac{2 - 0.3}{0.3} \times 100$

= 567% (to nearest whole number) *[1 mark]*

c) The urban population of more developed countries increased gradually from about 0.5 billion to 0.9 billion *[1 mark]*. The urban population of less developed countries was less than that of more developed in 1950 but much greater by 2000 *[1 mark]*. It increased rapidly from about 0.3 billion to 2 billion *[1 mark]*.

d) Any two from: e.g. urbanisation happened earlier in developed countries than in emerging and developing countries (e.g. during the industrial revolution) *[1 mark]* so most of the population now already live in urban areas *[1 mark]*. / Many people in developed countries prefer to live in rural areas *[1 mark]*. This means that many people are moving away from cities in developed countries *[1 mark]*. / De-industrialisation in cities in developed countries meant fewer jobs were available in manufacturing industries *[1 mark]*. Many people moved away from run-down cities to rural areas, so urban population growth slowed *[1 mark]*. / A lower proportion of the population in emerging and developing countries currently live in urban areas *[1 mark]*, so there are more people living in rural areas who might move to cities *[1 mark]*. / Many people in emerging and developing countries are moving to cities to get a better quality of life (e.g. access to better health care, jobs and education) *[1 mark]*. This is causing rapid urban growth in emerging and developing countries *[1 mark]*. / Emerging countries now have lots of manufacturing and service jobs *[1 mark]*. Many people in emerging countries are moving to urban areas to work in the new industries *[1 mark]*.

2 a) Any one from: e.g. overcrowding *[1 mark]* / congestion *[1 mark]* / increased air pollution from traffic *[1 mark]*

b) Any one from: e.g. high demand for houses and lack of space *[1 mark]* means that house prices can be very high *[1 mark]*. / High populations and a shortage of housing *[1 mark]* can lead to overcrowding *[1 mark]*. / High populations can make access to services more difficult *[1 mark]*, because the best schools may be oversubscribed/waiting times for health care may be long *[1 mark]*.

The question asks for 'one other effect', so if you put e.g. overcrowding for your answer to Q2a) you wouldn't get a mark if you put it again for part b).

3 a) B *[1 mark]*

Line graphs are often used for showing how something changes over time.

b) Any one from: e.g. there aren't enough homes for everyone so many people end up living in squatter settlements *[1 mark]* that are badly built and overcrowded *[1 mark]*. / People often don't have access to basic services, e.g. clean water, proper sewers or electricity *[1 mark]*. This can cause poor health *[1 mark]*.

c) Any one from: e.g. waste disposal services may not be able to keep pace with the growth, so rubbish may not all be collected or it may end up in big rubbish heaps *[1 mark]*. This can damage the environment, especially if the waste is toxic *[1 mark]*. / Sewage systems may not be able to cope with the increased number of people, so sewage and toxic chemicals can get into rivers *[1 mark]*, which can harm wildlife *[1 mark]*.

You could also have mentioned the higher number of vehicles on the roads, and the air pollution and greenhouse gas emissions that they cause.

Page 58: Urbanisation in the UK

1 a) i) The west and north of the UK generally have the fewest urban areas, so they have the lowest population density *[1 mark]*. The highest density of urban areas is found in the south east and the midlands, so these regions have the highest population density *[1 mark]*.

ii) A: Glasgow *[1 mark]*
B: London *[1 mark]*

iii) Any one from: e.g. upland regions such as the north of Scotland have few natural resources *[1 mark]*. / It is more difficult to build transport/infrastructure in upland regions such as the north of Scotland *[1 mark]*.

b) i) $\dfrac{64 + 74 + 78}{3} = \dfrac{216}{3} = 72\%$
[1 mark]

ii) Any two from: e.g. Reading has a higher employment rate than Blackburn, so there are likely to be more jobs available *[1 mark]*. People may be moving there to find work *[1 mark]*. / Reading has higher average weekly earnings *[1 mark]*, so people may be moving there to take up jobs with higher pay *[1 mark]*. / Reading is in the south of the UK, where service and high-tech industries are more likely to be located *[1 mark]*. These industries are creating more jobs, which attracts workers *[1 mark]*. / Blackburn is in the north of the UK, which was generally more negatively affected by de-industrialisation than the south *[1 mark]*. Jobs may be lower paid/there may be fewer jobs, attracting fewer people *[1 mark]*.

Pages 59-62: Urban Change — UK

1 a) i) inner city *[1 mark]*

De-industrialisation mainly affected inner city areas, where the people who worked in the factories lived. After the factories closed, people moved away, leaving empty buildings that were often vandalised, as seen in Figure 1.

ii) Your answer will depend on the city you have chosen. E.g. in London, de-industrialisation in the East End resulted in many workers in the docks and manufacturing industries becoming unemployed *[1 mark]*. This caused people to move away from the area *[1 mark]*, which meant many local services closed and buildings were left derelict *[1 mark]*. Derelict buildings became targets for graffiti and vandalism *[1 mark]*.

b) i) D *[1 mark]*

ii) Your answer will depend on the city you have chosen. E.g. in London, there are self-service bicycles and bike lanes *[1 mark]*, which helps to reduce noise and air pollution from motor vehicles *[1 mark]*. Barts Health NHS Trust is working with local communities to encourage healthy eating and regular exercise *[1 mark]*, which is improving people's health *[1 mark]*.

You might also have mentioned strategies to do with improving education or increasing employment opportunities.

2 a) Any two from: e.g. two railway stations *[1 mark]* / major roads *[1 mark]* / financial services *[1 mark]* / law firms *[1 mark]*

Component 2: The Human Environment

b) The movement of people back into urban areas *[1 mark]*.
c) The presence of financial services and law firms may have created new jobs attracting people who are looking for work *[1 mark]*. The arts and music centre may have attracted young people who want to live close to good entertainment services *[1 mark]*.

3 a) C *[1 mark]*
For the 21-30 age group, the 'Migration to London' line is higher than the 'Migration out of London' line — more people moved to London than moved away, so the population of this age group must have increased.
b) People aged 21-30 are likely to have children *[1 mark]*, so the population may be growing due to natural increase *[1 mark]*.
c) Your answer will depend on the city you have chosen.
Any one from: e.g. young people are moving to London from within the UK *[1 mark]* in order to find work or to study *[1 mark]*. / Many migrants from the EU have come to London to work *[1 mark]* because the EU allows free movement between its member countries *[1 mark]*.
You could have also mentioned non-EU migrants who often come to cities in the UK to study or to be with family.
d) Your answer will depend on the city you have chosen.
E.g. in London, immigration is leading to overcrowding in some inner city areas *[1 mark]* because poorer immigrants often live in council tower blocks and older terraces which are more affordable *[1 mark]*. The age structure of inner city London is being altered by immigration *[1 mark]* because it is mainly young adults who are moving there *[1 mark]*.
You could also have written about the impact of immigration on services (e.g. education or health care) or ethnic diversity.

4 a) The movement of shops and businesses out of the CBD to locations on the edge of town *[1 mark]*.
b) Hamhall Shopping Centre/Hamslow Business Park is located on the outskirts of Hamslow *[1 mark]*.
c) Any one from: e.g. better transport links, e.g. the development of the M99/new rail lines and stations *[1 mark]* may have improved access to locations on the edge of town, making them more desirable *[1 mark]*. / Increased car ownership *[1 mark]* may have led to congestion in the city centre, making edge-of-town locations more attractive to businesses *[1 mark]*.

5 a) The population is increasing so there is a high demand for houses *[1 mark]*. However, the number of houses built has slightly decreased on average over the same period *[1 mark]*. House prices have also increased, making it harder for poorer people to buy their own home *[1 mark]*.
b) Your answer will depend on the city you have chosen.
E.g. houses in the BedZED development in south London have thick insulation, solar heating systems and water-saving appliances *[1 mark]*. This helps to reduce energy consumption and conserve resources *[1 mark]*.

6 This question is level marked. There are 4 extra marks available for spelling, punctuation and grammar.
How to grade your answer:
Level 0: There is no relevant information. *[0 marks]*
Level 1: There is a basic description of at least one way that quality of life varies in the city, with an attempt to link it to economic change. *[1-3 marks]*
Level 2: There is a clear explanation of how at least two aspects of quality of life have been affected by economic change. The answer attempts to identify the most important impacts. *[4-6 marks]*
Level 3: There is a detailed explanation of a range of ways that quality of life varies across the city and they are clearly linked to economic changes that have taken place there. The answer clearly identifies the most important impacts. *[7-8 marks]*
Make sure your spelling, punctuation and grammar are consistently correct, that your meaning is clear and that you use a range of geographical terms correctly *[0-4 marks]*
Your answer must refer to a named example.

Here are some points your answer may include:
• A brief introduction explaining that economic change is increasing inequality in your chosen city, and that it is affecting quality of life in the city.
• An explanation of the economic changes that have taken place in the city, e.g. de-industrialisation, the growth of service or high-tech industries.
• How the economic changes have increased inequality, e.g. increases in the number of very high paying jobs along with unemployment and low wages.
• How this affects quality of life in the city including a judgement about how severe the impact is, e.g. pressure on services in poorer areas where councils have less money, which may make access to good education and health care more difficult. Unhealthy lifestyles in poorer areas lead to people suffering from bad health and lower life expectancies.
• A brief conclusion summing up the impact that economic change has had on quality of life in your chosen city. An overall judgement about which factor has had the biggest impact.
• Your answer could refer to London, where a combination of de-industrialisation and the growth of high-paying financial jobs have led to big differences in wealth and therefore quality of life. 25% of the population are living in poverty and life expectancy is 5 years lower in poorer areas of the city than in wealthy areas. Poverty has led to lack of choice in housing and schools, and may affect access to health care.

Pages 63-65: Urban Change — Global

1 a)

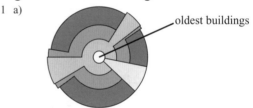

[1 mark]
b) The rural-urban fringe / outskirts *[1 mark]*
c) The inner city *[1 mark]*
d) E.g. industry may have located along major roads or rivers *[1 mark]* so it is easier to transport goods into and out of the city *[1 mark]*.

2 a) Any two from: e.g. Figure 2 shows children in school uniform — cities offer better access to services such as education compared to rural areas *[1 mark]*. / Figure 2 shows electricity and telephone cables connecting buildings — access to resources such as electricity is better in cities than in rural areas *[1 mark]*. / There are motorbikes parked outside the buildings in Figure 2, showing that people are reasonably wealthy — cities offer more jobs and better wages than rural areas *[1 mark]*.
The question tells you to use the figure, so make sure you comment on reasons for rural-urban migration that you can identify from the photo.
b) When the birth rate is higher than the death rate, more people are born than are dying so the population grows *[1 mark]*.
c) Any one from: e.g. wars or conflict can cause people to leave neighbouring countries in search of safety *[1 mark]*. / Poverty and poor quality of life might cause people to leave neighbouring countries in search of better jobs *[1 mark]*. / People from foreign countries might come to set up or work in branches of TNCs *[1 mark]*.
TNCs are transnational corporations — this means they operate in more than one country.

3 a) E.g. it is likely that there are lots of poor people moving to the cities who can't afford good quality housing *[1 mark]*, so they have to live in slums on undesirable land *[1 mark]*. The wealthy can afford better housing *[1 mark]*, so can live in high-class housing with good access to services *[1 mark]*.
You could also talk about the inequalities in waste disposal and exposure to pollution or the impact of living conditions on people's health.

Answers

Component 2: The Human Environment

b) Your answer will depend on the city you have chosen.
E.g. in Lagos, the government has begun work on new water treatment plants and distribution networks *[1 mark]*, so more people have access to clean, piped water *[1 mark]*. They are also investing in training and education programmes (e.g. ReadySetWork) *[1 mark]* to ensure that young people are employable when they leave school or university *[1 mark]*.
You could also have written about environmental improvements, e.g. increasing recycling or reducing pollution.

4 a) i) A settlement that is built illegally in and around a city by people who can't afford proper housing *[1 mark]*.
You may have worded your definition slightly differently. That's fine as long as you mention that the houses are built illegally or that people don't own the land they build on.

ii) Any two from: e.g. they can face eviction *[1 mark]* if the settlements are demolished to clean up the city *[1 mark]*. / Electricity can often cut out *[1 mark]* because it is accessed through illegal connections *[1 mark]*. / There are high levels of crime *[1 mark]*, e.g. because of high unemployment *[1 mark]*.

iii) Any one from: e.g. there is often a lack of jobs leading to high levels of unemployment *[1 mark]*. Formal jobs may have long working hours and low pay *[1 mark]*. / There may be limited waste collection services *[1 mark]*, meaning rubbish piles up on the streets, creating health risks *[1 mark]*. / There may not be proper sewage systems *[1 mark]*. Sewage may be left in the streets or emptied into water courses leading to health risks *[1 mark]*. / There may be high levels of air pollution *[1 mark]* from traffic congestion/emissions from factories causing health risks *[1 mark]*.

b) i) E.g. the projects are usually on a smaller scale than top-down projects so reach fewer people *[1 mark]*. / Funds may be limited, especially during economic recessions, when the strategy may be needed the most *[1 mark]*. / They can lack coordination because there may be several organisations with the same aims working separately *[1 mark]*.

ii) This question is level marked. There are 4 extra marks available for spelling, punctuation and grammar.
How to grade your answer:
Level 0: There is no relevant information. *[0 marks]*
Level 1: There is a basic description of at least one strategy used to improve quality of life in the city. *[1-3 marks]*
Level 2: There is a clear explanation of two or more strategies that have been used to improve quality of life in the city, and an attempt to assess how effective they were. *[4-6 marks]*
Level 3: There is a detailed explanation of a range of strategies used to improve quality of life in the city and a clear assessment of how effective they were. *[7-8 marks]*
Make sure your spelling, punctuation and grammar are consistently correct, that your meaning is clear and that you use a range of geographical terms correctly *[0-4 marks]*.
Your answer must refer to a named example.
Here are some points your answer may include:
• A brief description of your chosen city and the problems it faces.
• The pros and cons of bottom-up and top-down approaches.
• An assessment of examples of top-down strategies in your chosen city, such as attempts by governments to improve water supply and waste disposal.
• An assessment of examples of bottom-up strategies in your chosen city, such as attempts by communities and NGOs to improve health and education.
• A conclusion that summarises the effectiveness of the strategies used, e.g. in general, bottom-up strategies have been more effective than top-down strategies at improving quality of life.

• Your answer could refer to Lagos, Nigeria, where many strategies have been undertaken, with varying levels of effectiveness. E.g. the government banned the import of small electricity generators to reduce air pollution. However, the ban negatively affected some poorer people, as they were less able to afford cleaner alternatives. Therefore this strategy was limited in its effectiveness.

Topic 5 — Global Development

Page 66: Measuring Development

1 a) A *[1 mark]*
b) 43.7 − 10.2 = 33.5 *[1 mark]*
The range is just the difference between the highest and lowest value.
c) E.g. individual indicators can be misleading if they are used on their own because as a country develops, some aspects develop before others *[1 mark]*. HDI is calculated using several different indicators, so it is likely to give a much more accurate idea of how developed a country is *[1 mark]*.
d) The Corruption Perceptions Index (CPI) *[1 mark]* is a measure of the level of corruption in the public sector on a scale of 1-100 where a lower score indicates more corruption *[1 mark]*. Less developed countries generally have more corruption, so a lower CPI score *[1 mark]*.
e) E.g. Canada is the most developed country *[1 mark]*. It has the highest HDI score, so has the highest level of human development *[1 mark]*. Canada has a higher GDP per capita than Malaysia or Angola, suggesting that its citizens are wealthy *[1 mark]*. It also has the lowest Gini coefficient score, so it has the lowest level of economic inequality *[1 mark]*.
You might also have mentioned that Canada has a high life expectancy, suggesting that health care there is good. It's also got a low birth rate, which suggests that sexual health care (e.g. contraceptives) may be more widely accessible.

Page 67: Global Development

1 a) i) E.g. Libya has a very dry climate — more than 90% of the country is desert or semi-desert *[1 mark]*. This probably means that it can't grow much food *[1 mark]*. This can lead to malnutrition, which reduces people's quality of life *[1 mark]*.
Alternatively you could have said that with fewer crops to sell, people have less money to spend on goods and services, which also reduces their quality of life.
ii) Any one from: e.g. lack of raw materials, such as coal, oil or metal ores *[1 mark]* means countries make less money because they have fewer products to sell *[1 mark]*. / Countries with lots of natural hazards may struggle to develop *[1 mark]*, because they have to spend a lot of money rebuilding after disasters occur instead of investing in development *[1 mark]*.
You might also have written that landlocked countries (countries without a coastline) can struggle to develop because it can be harder and more expensive to transport goods into and out of the country.
b) Any two from: e.g. poor trade links *[1 mark]* / debt *[1 mark]* / primary products as main exports *[1 mark]*
Countries that mostly export primary products tend to be less developed because you don't make much profit selling primary products. The prices also tend to fluctuate, so sometimes the price falls below the cost of production.
c) Countries that were colonised often have a lower level of development when they gain independence than they would if they had not been colonised *[1 mark]*. This is because colonisers control the economies of their colonies, e.g. by exploiting raw materials *[1 mark]*. The money made goes to the colonising country, so it is not used to develop the colonised country, which remains relatively undeveloped *[1 mark]*.

Page 68: UK Development

1 a) Life expectancy is highest in the south of the UK and lowest in Scotland *[1 mark]*. It is also relatively low in northern England *[1 mark]*.
b) Any one from: e.g. wealth *[1 mark]* / educational attainment *[1 mark]* / unemployment *[1 mark]* / average wages *[1 mark]*

Component 2: The Human Environment

2 a) Any one from: e.g. the quality of housing in the photograph of Bath is higher than that in the photograph of Chadderton *[1 mark]*. / There are several factories in the photograph of Chadderton, whereas the photograph of Bath includes more offices and shops, which usually provide better-paid jobs *[1 mark]*.

You won't get the mark for giving evidence that can't be seen in the photo.

b) Any two from: e.g. the growth of post-industrial service industries has mostly benefited the south *[1 mark]*, so there are more better-paid jobs *[1 mark]*. / The decline of heavy industry has had a greater negative impact on the north of the UK than the south *[1 mark]*, so unemployment tends to be high and wages low *[1 mark]*. / It's more difficult to develop transport infrastructure in the north and west where it tends to be mountainous *[1 mark]*, so there are fewer industries and fewer jobs available *[1 mark]*. / Southern regions of the UK have better transport links to mainland Europe and the rest of the world *[1 mark]*, so there are better trade opportunities in the south *[1 mark]*.

You could have also mentioned less productive farming in the north and west of the UK, London's status as a global financial centre and its influence on the surrounding regions, or government policies that have helped to increase economic growth in some areas.

Page 69: Effects of Uneven Development

1 a) When people are able to eat enough nutritious food to stay healthy and active *[1 mark]*.

b) E.g. people in less developed countries are quite likely to live in slum housing if they live in urban areas *[1 mark]*. For example, 74.4% of the urban population of Haiti live in slums *[1 mark]*. Slum housing is often flimsy and lacks connections to services, such as proper sanitation facilities *[1 mark]*.

You might also have mentioned that a lack of building regulations in less developed countries can lead to poor quality housing that is vulnerable to damage through natural disasters.

c) E.g. infant mortality is higher in developing countries, such as Haiti *[1 mark]* and Haiti has fewer hospital beds than the UK, suggesting that there is a more limited health care system *[1 mark]*. Poorer people can struggle to access enough quality food to keep them healthy *[1 mark]*. For example, 45.8% of the population of Haiti are undernourished compared to 2.5% in the UK *[1 mark]*.

You could also have written about how lack of sanitation facilities leads to water-borne diseases such as diarrhoea and cholera.

d) Less developed countries can't afford to invest as much in education as developed countries *[1 mark]*. Poorer people may not be able to afford school fees/children may have to work instead of attending school *[1 mark]*. Lack of education means people can't get better-paid, skilled jobs in the future *[1 mark]*. Lots of people in developing countries work in low-skilled service jobs or in factories where pay is low, hours are long and conditions can be dangerous *[1 mark]*.

You could also have mentioned that a high percentage of people in developing countries are employed in the primary sector where conditions are also poor.

Page 70: Increasing Development

1 a) D *[1 mark]*

b) Any one from: e.g. inter-governmental agreements are when the governments of several different countries work together to increase development *[1 mark]*. They may involve inter-governmental organisations (IGOs), such as the World Bank *[1 mark]*. IGOs can set global goals for development, such as the Millennium Development Goals *[1 mark]*. / International aid is money or resources given by one country or organisation to a different country *[1 mark]*. Some aid is spent on development projects such as building dams and wells to improve clean water supplies *[1 mark]*. Short term aid is given to help countries cope with emergencies *[1 mark]*.

c) Any two from: e.g. projects led by local communities are designed to address the needs of people in that community *[1 mark]*. / They make use of locally available, cheap materials, so the community isn't dependent on expensive imports *[1 mark]*. / Projects often employ local people, so they earn money and learn new skills *[1 mark]*.

d) E.g. the projects are often very expensive *[1 mark]*, and there may be conditions for borrowing the money, e.g. paying back loans with interest *[1 mark]*. The projects are often high-tech and energy intensive *[1 mark]*. This means that the host country becomes dependent on technology and workers from richer countries *[1 mark]*.

Pages 71-74: Developing and Emerging Countries

1 a)

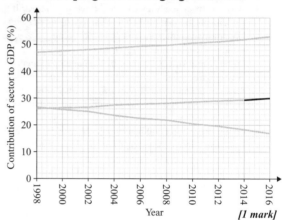

[1 mark]

b) $\dfrac{\text{\% of total GDP}}{100} \times \text{total GDP}$

$= \dfrac{17}{100} \times 1.9 \text{ trillion}$ *[1 mark]*

$= \text{US\$ } 0.32 \text{ trillion (2 d.p.)}$ *[1 mark]*

There are different ways that you could show your working out for 1 b). As long as you show your working and get the right answer, you'll get full marks.

c) Any one from: e.g. agriculture/farming *[1 mark]* / fishing *[1 mark]* / mining *[1 mark]* / forestry *[1 mark]*

Primary industry involves getting raw materials/natural resources from the earth.

d) **Advantage**: any one from: e.g. the increase in secondary industry may provide people with more reliable jobs compared to seasonal agricultural work *[1 mark]*. / The increase in secondary industry may bring more money into the country than selling raw materials does *[1 mark]*. / The increase in services may provide better paid work with better conditions than work in the primary or secondary sectors *[1 mark]*.

Disadvantage: any one from: e.g. decreased investment in the primary sector along with population growth may lead to workers becoming unemployed *[1 mark]*. / Jobs in secondary industries may be dangerous or conditions may be poor *[1 mark]*. / Changes in the type of jobs available in service industries can lead to a lack of job security for unskilled workers *[1 mark]*.

e) Your answer will vary depending on the country you have chosen. E.g. in India, trade is becoming increasingly important to the economy *[1 mark]*. Since 1991, the government has reduced barriers to trade, so trade with foreign businesses is increasing *[1 mark]*. India is part of the World Trade Organisation and a member of G20, which increase its opportunities for trade *[1 mark]*.

2 a) E.g. there were more people in total in 2010 than in 1980 *[1 mark]*. In 1980 there was a high proportion of children/the pyramid had a concave shape, whereas in 2010 there population was more evenly distributed between each age group/the base of the pyramid is narrowing and the top is widening *[1 mark]*. In 1980 there weren't any people aged over 80 but by 2010 there were approximately 0.3 million people aged over 80 *[1 mark]*.

Component 2: The Human Environment

b) Any two from: e.g. there may be better health care *[1 mark]*, which means people are living longer/infant mortality is reduced, so there are more older/working age people *[1 mark]*. / Women may have a more equal place in society/be getting a better education so spend more time working *[1 mark]*, so they may be having fewer children, leading to a lower proportion of children *[1 mark]*. / The use of contraception may be increasing *[1 mark]*, so women may be having fewer children, leading to a lower proportion of children *[1 mark]*.

3 a)

Mobile phone subscriptions (per 100 people) — Mali, Botswana, 2005, 2015

[1 mark]

b) 157 − 30 = 127 *[1 mark]*

You'd get a mark if your answer was anywhere between 126 and 128 — the top of the 2015 bar for Botswana is somewhere between 156 and 158.

c) Any one from: e.g. increasing personal wealth in emerging and developing countries *[1 mark]* means that more people can afford to own mobile phones *[1 mark]*. / There are an increasing range of uses for mobile phones, e.g. online banking *[1 mark]*, so people in emerging and developing countries can use them to improve their lives (particularly in remote rural locations) *[1 mark]*.

d) Your answer will vary depending on the country you have chosen. E.g. In India, some people have been able to start their own small businesses *[1 mark]* because they can now make and receive payments online and don't need to travel long distances to go to banks *[1 mark]*.

e) This question is level marked. How to grade your answer:

Level 0: There is no relevant information. *[0 marks]*

Level 1: There is a basic description of inequality in the chosen country. *[1-3 marks]*

Level 2: There is a clear assessment of inequality and at least one other social change taking place in the chosen country. There is an attempt to draw a conclusion about which is the most important. *[4-6 marks]*

Level 3: There is a detailed assessment of inequality and the other social changes taking place in the chosen country. There is a clear conclusion about which is the most important, supported with evidence. *[7-8 marks]*

Your answer must refer to a named example.

Here are some points your answer may include:
- A brief introduction describing how economic development has led to an increase in inequality.
- The extent of inequality in the chosen country, e.g. how new wealth has gone to richer people, whilst the poorest people stay poor.
- An assessment of how much of an impact increasing inequality has had on the chosen country.
- Other social changes, e.g. the growing middle class and improvements in education.
- An assessment of how much of an impact each change has had on the chosen country.
- A brief conclusion that states which change has been the most important for the country, supported by evidence from the main body of your answer.

- Your answer could refer to India, where economic development has increased inequality — there are many multimillionaires but 40% of employed people earn less than US $3.10 a day. However, more people have been able to find work in higher paid jobs enabling them to be able to buy consumer goods, e.g. mobile phones. Education has also improved and 96% of children now enrol for school.

4 a) The level of private investment stayed around the same level (about US$ 4 million) between 2008 and 2011 *[1 mark]* before increasing rapidly between 2011 and 2016 to US$ 34 million *[1 mark]*.

b) i) Your answer will vary depending on the country you have chosen. E.g. large TNCs outsource manufacturing and IT to India *[1 mark]*. This is increasing employment opportunities, so people have more money to spend on improving their quality of life *[1 mark]*. It is also increasing the amount of income from tax for the Indian government *[1 mark]*, so they have more money to spend on improving services such as health care and education *[1 mark]*.

ii) Your answer will vary depending on the country you have chosen. E.g. in India, the government has developed the Act East policy to increase its influence over countries in southeast Asia *[1 mark]*. This is increasing trade opportunities and encouraging foreign companies to invest in India *[1 mark]*.

5 a) A *[1 mark]*

Peripheral areas in developing countries often benefit less from economic development than core areas. This means that access to health care, education and well-paid employment is usually worse in peripheral areas.

b) E.g. the growth in manufacturing and services associated with economic development is often concentrated in core urban areas more than peripheral rural areas *[1 mark]*. This means that the GDP per capita increases more in core urban areas because that's where new and better paid jobs are created *[1 mark]*.

c) E.g. the literacy rate is usually lower in areas of a developing country where access to education is lower *[1 mark]*. Access to education is usually lower in peripheral areas, which benefit less economically from development *[1 mark]*.

You could also write about children in peripheral areas having less access to education because they're more likely to need to work to make money for the family rather than go to school.

d) Your answer will vary depending on the country you have chosen. E.g. in India, the government is investing in a large scale solar park scheme *[1 mark]*, which aims to increase the number of people who have access to electricity *[1 mark]*. They are also planning smart cities with affordable, energy-efficient housing and better infrastructure *[1 mark]*, so that economic growth continues, providing better jobs for a greater number of people *[1 mark]*.

e) This question is level marked. There are 4 extra marks available for spelling, punctuation and grammar.

How to grade your answer:

Level 0: There is no relevant information. *[0 marks]*

Level 1: There is a basic description of the positive or negative impacts of rapid development on people. *[1-3 marks]*

Level 2: There is a clear explanation of the positive and negative impacts of rapid development on people. There is an attempt to draw conclusions. *[4-6 marks]*

Level 3: There is a detailed and comprehensive discussion about the positive and negative impacts of rapid development on people. There is a clear conclusion, supported with evidence. *[7-8 marks]*

Make sure your spelling, punctuation and grammar are consistently correct, that your meaning is clear and that you use a range of geographical terms correctly *[0-4 marks]*.

Your answer must refer to a named example.

Component 2: The Human Environment

Here are some points your answer may include:

- The positive impacts of rapid development on people including economic, social and environmental effects, e.g. more jobs available, making people wealthier and enabling them to access services such as better health care.
- The negative impacts of rapid development on people including economic, social and environmental effects, e.g. that housing and infrastructure can't be built fast enough to keep up with rising urban populations, so lots of people end up living in slums, and increased energy consumption leading to high levels of air pollution.
- A conclusion that states whether rapid development has had an overall positive or negative impact on people, supported with evidence from the main body of your answer.
- Your answer could refer to India, where daily wages increased by about 18% between 2011 and 2014, so people have more money to improve their quality of life. Some TNCs are also running development programs to help people in rural villages become entrepreneurs. However, almost a quarter of the urban population live in slums and some jobs have poor conditions, reducing workers' quality of life. TNCs have been accused of moving around to take advantage of local tax breaks. Air pollution is high with the 10 most polluted cities in the world all being in India, which is causing health problems for people living in polluted areas.

Topic 6 — Resource Management

Page 75: Natural Resources

1 a) Any two from: e.g. water *[1 mark]* / coal *[1 mark]* / oil *[1 mark]* / gas *[1 mark]* / minerals *[1 mark]*

b) A *[1 mark]*

c) Any one from: e.g. waste from mines can pollute groundwater *[1 mark]*. / Habitats can be destroyed to make way for mines *[1 mark]*.

d) Any one from: e.g. building dams can prevent the seasonal migration of species in rivers *[1 mark]*. / Building dams can flood valleys, which destroys habitats *[1 mark]*.

2 a) E.g. removing hedgerows to clear space for crops *[1 mark]* can reduce biodiversity by destroying the habitats of plant and animal species *[1 mark]*.

b) E.g. through the use of heavy machinery for planting and harvesting *[1 mark]*.

Page 76: UK Distribution of Resources

1 a) 6744 *[1 mark]*

b) Any one from: e.g. it is an upland area in the UK *[1 mark]*, so it is likely to have high rainfall *[1 mark]*. / It is a steep-sided valley *[1 mark]*, so it's suitable for damming *[1 mark]*. / The steep terrain *[1 mark]* means that streams and rivers in the area are fast-flowing *[1 mark]*.

You can tell it is an upland area from the numbers on the contour lines — the shores of the reservoir are at 190 metres above sea level.

c) E.g. rocks/minerals *[1 mark]*, timber *[1 mark]*

2 a) E.g. hill sheep farming is mainly distributed in the north and west of the UK *[1 mark]*, especially Wales, northern England, and north west Scotland *[1 mark]*.

b) Any one from: e.g. these areas are flatter *[1 mark]*, which makes them suited to the use of farm machinery *[1 mark]*. / These areas have more fertile soils *[1 mark]*, which helps crops grow well *[1 mark]*. / These areas have warmer, sunnier summers *[1 mark]*, which help crops grow *[1 mark]*.

Pages 77-78: Global Distribution & Consumption of Resources

1 a) C *[1 mark]*

b) E.g. some regions have climates which are better suited to growing crops, e.g. they receive lots of rain and sunshine *[1 mark]*.

2 a) i) UK *[1 mark]*

ii) 6 400 terawatt-hours *[1 mark]*

iii) China *[1 mark]* because it had high oil consumption but relatively low oil production/it had the biggest difference between the amount of oil consumed and the amount of oil produced *[1 mark]*.

b) E.g. developed countries generally consume more energy than developing countries because people there are wealthier *[1 mark]*, so they can afford a lifestyle that uses more energy *[1 mark]*.

You could also have mentioned that developed countries tend to have more industry, which can consume a lot of energy.

3 a) 1761 + 1522 + 285 + 534 + 1220 = 5322
5322 ÷ 5 = 1064.4 mm (accept 1064) *[1 mark]*

b) E.g. Brazil has higher average annual rainfall than Chile *[1 mark]*, so it might have more water resources than Chile *[1 mark]*. Chile has a higher GNI per capita than Brazil *[1 mark]*, and wealthier people tend to use more water e.g. through the use of washing machines *[1 mark]*.

4 a) C *[1 mark]*

b) E.g. Country C is at a higher level of development than Country B, so more people there have a higher income *[1 mark]* and are able to buy more food *[1 mark]*.

Energy Resource Management

Pages 79-80: Meeting Energy Demand

1 a) E.g. non-renewable energy sources can't be replenished quickly, so they can run out *[1 mark]*.

b) E.g. oil has been used to generate energy for a long time *[1 mark]*, so it is an energy source which has been proven to work *[1 mark]*.

2 a) E.g. more people can afford devices and appliances which use lots of energy *[1 mark]*.

b) Any one from: e.g. used nuclear fuel is very radioactive and toxic *[1 mark]*, so it can pollute the environment if it is not properly contained *[1 mark]*. / Mining for uranium removes soil and vegetation *[1 mark]*, which destroys habitats and reduces biodiversity *[1 mark]*.

c) i) E.g. fracking is a way of extracting natural gas that is trapped in shale rock underground *[1 mark]* by pumping liquid into the shale rock at high pressure *[1 mark]*. This causes the rock to crack, releasing the gas *[1 mark]*.

ii) E.g. fracking provides a way of reaching gas reserves that were previously unexploited *[1 mark]*, so it could help meet energy demands when other fossil fuel reserves are depleted *[1 mark]*.

3 a) Location: C *[1 mark]*
Reason: any one from: e.g. C is exposed on all sides, so turbines will be powered by wind from all directions *[1 mark]*. / It is high up, where winds are stronger *[1 mark]*. / It is located away from urban areas, so people won't be affected by noise pollution *[1 mark]*.

Locations A, B and E are ruled out because they are sheltered by hills, buildings or trees. Location D is ruled out because it is offshore.

b) E.g. habitats in the woodland would be destroyed to make space for the solar farm *[1 mark]*.

c) E.g. wind farms produce a constant humming noise, which causes noise pollution for people living nearby *[1 mark]*.

d) Your answer will depend on the renewable energy resource that you have chosen. E.g. generating wind energy doesn't produce CO_2 *[1 mark]*, so it doesn't contribute to global warming and climate change *[1 mark]*. Wind turbines can be installed by individuals or local communities *[1 mark]*, which benefits the local economy *[1 mark]*.

Page 81: The Energy Mix

1 a) Coal *[1 mark]*

b) Gas *[1 mark]*

Component 2: The Human Environment

c) E.g. the UK's energy mix changed between 1970 and 2014, but continued to rely mostly on fossil fuels *[1 mark]*. In 1970, the biggest source of energy in the UK was coal, but in 2014 gas was more significant *[1 mark]*. In 1970, 97% of the UK's energy mix was based on fossil fuels, but in 2014, 15% of the UK's energy came from nuclear and renewable sources *[1 mark]*.

d) i) E.g. people with more money can afford to invest in renewable energy for their homes, e.g. installing solar panels on their roofs *[1 mark]*. Governments in developed countries have more money to invest in e.g. nuclear plants and large-scale wind/solar farms, which tend to be relatively expensive to build *[1 mark]*.

ii) E.g. a country with a rapidly growing population needs to generate lots of energy as quickly as possible *[1 mark]* so it is more likely to use fossil fuel energy sources, as they have historically been cheaper/easier/quicker to develop than nuclear or renewable sources *[1 mark]*.

iii) E.g. the availability of energy resources *[1 mark]*.

Some countries have greater access to particular energy resources than others. For these countries, the resources they have access to are likely to make up a bigger proportion of their energy mix. E.g. in 2016 the US got 73% of its energy from oil and gas, because it has large oil reserves and has invested a lot of money in fracking.

Page 82: Sustainable Energy Management

1 a) E.g. they might be in favour of the exploitation of coal, as it provides a cheap supply of energy *[1 mark]*. They might not want to have a coal-fired power plant near their house because of the pollution that burning coal causes *[1 mark]*.

b) i) E.g. providing energy today without preventing future generations from meeting their energy needs *[1 mark]*.

ii) E.g. demand for energy is increasing but non-renewable energy resources are running out *[1 mark]*.

You could also mention that consuming fossil fuels releases greenhouse gases, which cause climate change.

c) E.g. environmental organisations, such as Greenpeace, might promote the use of renewable energy resources *[1 mark]* to reduce the negative environmental impacts of extracting and burning fossil fuels *[1 mark]*. Governments might also be looking into developing renewable resources for the future *[1 mark]*, in order to secure energy supplies in the long-term *[1 mark]*.

d) This question is level marked. There are 4 extra marks available for spelling, punctuation and grammar.
How to grade your answer:

Level 0: There is no relevant information. *[0 marks]*

Level 1: There is a basic description of how countries with contrasting levels of development have attempted to manage their energy resources sustainably. *[1-3 marks]*

Level 2: There is a clear description of how countries with contrasting levels of development have attempted to manage their energy resources sustainably. There is a brief assessment of how the countries' levels of development have affected these strategies. *[4-6 marks]*

Level 3: There is a detailed description of how countries with contrasting levels of development have attempted to manage their energy resources sustainably. There is a considered assessment of how the countries' levels of development have affected these strategies. *[7-8 marks]*

Make sure your spelling, punctuation and grammar are consistently correct, that your meaning is clear and that you use a range of geographical terms correctly *[0-4 marks]*.
Your answer must refer to named examples.
Here are some points your answer may include:
• A brief description of the level of development in your chosen countries.

• Strategies that have been used in each country to attempt to manage energy resources sustainably, e.g. the development of renewable energy resources, changes to infrastructure, legislation and technological innovation.

• An assessment of the differences between management strategies in each country, and how these differences relate to the country's level of development, e.g. whether the government of each country has the resources to develop infrastructure, or whether individuals can afford technologies which reduce their energy consumption.

• E.g. your answer could refer to Sweden and India. The government of Sweden has a 'green electricity certification' strategy, which involves making sure that companies which sell electricity have to buy a proportion of the electricity from renewable sources. The Swedish government has set the target of getting 100% of its electricity from renewable energy resources by 2040. Sweden is a developed country, so many of its citizens can afford technologies that help to reduce their energy consumption, e.g. electric cars. In India, the government has pledged to double the amount of renewable energy it generates by 2030, which would account for 40% of its energy. India has also introduced measures to reduce the use of cars in cities, in order to reduce fuel consumption and air pollution. India is an emerging country, and many rural communities are not connected to the national energy grid, so some communities have set up their own renewable energy projects.

Water Resource Management

Pages 83-84: Global Water Distribution and Consumption

1 a) B *[1 mark]*

b) E.g. as the country developed, it's likely that the industrial sector grew *[1 mark]*, so the country may have needed more water for industry and less for agriculture *[1 mark]*.

2 a) Canada *[1 mark]*

b) Any one from: Mexico has a high population density of 65 people per km^2 *[1 mark]*, so there is not enough water available to meet the needs of the whole population *[1 mark]*. / Mexico has a high average temperature of 20.9 °C *[1 mark]*, so it probably has high rates of evaporation *[1 mark]*.

c) Canada has a low population density, so demand for water is relatively low *[1 mark]*. Although Canada receives less rainfall than the USA or Mexico, the climate there is cooler *[1 mark]*, so less water is lost to evaporation *[1 mark]*.

d) E.g. climate change is causing rainfall to become less reliable in some areas *[1 mark]*, so there is less surface water available/ water stores aren't being replenished *[1 mark]*.

You could also have mentioned that increased temperatures in some areas are increasing evaporation of surface water.

3 a) $320 - 50 = 270$ cubic metres *[1 mark]*

b) 52% *[1 mark]*

$$\frac{380 - 250}{250} \times 100 = 52$$

c) Any two from: e.g. people may have become wealthier *[1 mark]*, and so adopted a lifestyle that uses more water, e.g. using washing machines *[1 mark]*. / Emerging countries often have a growing industrial sector *[1 mark]*. Industrial processes tend to use a lot of water *[1 mark]*. / Farmers may have become wealthier *[1 mark]*, and so adopted agricultural practices that use more water, e.g. irrigation *[1 mark]*.

d) E.g. Country B has much lower water withdrawals per person than Country A *[1 mark]*. People in developing countries may not have convenient or affordable access to clean water, so they tend to use less water *[1 mark]*.

You might also have said that developing countries often have fewer industries, which use a lot of water, so they don't need as much water as emerging or developed countries.

Component 3: Geographical Investigations

Page 85: Water Supply Problems

1 a) Any one from: e.g. the north west of the UK has the biggest supply of water because it has high rainfall *[1 mark]*, but the highest demand for water is in the south east and the Midlands, because they have high population densities *[1 mark]*. / The UK has seasonal imbalances in water supply and demand *[1 mark]*. In the winter, rainfall is high and demand is low, whereas in the summer, rainfall is low and demand is high *[1 mark]*. / The UK's water infrastructure is ageing and struggling to carry the volumes of water needed to meet demand *[1 mark]*. A lot of water is also lost through leaking pipes *[1 mark]*.

b) E.g. reservoirs can be used to store water in the winter, when rainfall is high *[1 mark]*, to be used in the summer, when rainfall is lower but demand is higher *[1 mark]*.

Reservoirs can also be used to collect water so it can be transferred from areas with high rainfall and low demand to areas with higher demand.

2 a) E.g. the children are gathering water from a puddle/open pool rather than a safe, treated source *[1 mark]*.

b) Any one from: e.g. drinking untreated water may cause people to become ill or die from water-borne diseases like dysentery *[1 mark]*. / People have to spend time carrying water to their homes *[1 mark]*.

c) Any one from: e.g. many emerging and developing countries are located in areas with low rainfall *[1 mark]* and may lack the technology and infrastructure to store the rainfall they do receive *[1 mark]*. / Many emerging and development countries lack adequate water treatment facilities *[1 mark]*, so many people have to use untreated water *[1 mark]*. / There may be a lack of infrastructure for treating sewage and waste water *[1 mark]*, which means there is a greater risk of water supplies being polluted *[1 mark]*.

Page 86: Exploiting Water Resources

1 a) 760 – 318 = 442 cubic metres *[1 mark]*

b) 4.44 billion cubic metres *[1 mark]*

The median is the middle value (when values are in order of size).

c) E.g. the government might be concerned that there could be water shortages *[1 mark]* due to the decreasing water supplies per capita and increasing demand for water *[1 mark]*.

The government might also be concerned about how to promote industrial growth whilst managing industrial water consumption.

d) E.g. both individuals and businesses are likely to want to have enough water to meet their needs *[1 mark]*. Individuals might think that the main priority for water consumption is to provide a supply of water that is clean, safe and easily available *[1 mark]*, whereas businesses need a cheap and plentiful supply of water to make sure they make a profit, even if this means exploiting water unsustainably *[1 mark]*.

e) E.g. desalination *[1 mark]* could be used to remove salt from sea water in order to increase Algeria's freshwater resources *[1 mark]*.

Page 87: Sustainable Water Management

1 a) E.g. in Figure 1, individuals are recycling 'grey' water from showers, sinks and washing machines *[1 mark]* to use for flushing toilets and watering their gardens *[1 mark]*. This makes their water use more sustainable because less water needs to be extracted from rivers or from groundwater to meet their needs *[1 mark]*.

b) Any two from: e.g. individuals may support the sustainable management of water *[1 mark]* as they want to make sure that they have access to enough clean water in the future *[1 mark]*. / Environmental organisations may argue that people should use water more sustainably *[1 mark]* to make sure that there is enough water to sustain wildlife populations *[1 mark]*. / Industrial organisations may promote the use of technologies which create alternative or more efficient water supplies *[1 mark]*, as this helps them save money on production costs *[1 mark]*.

c) E.g. countries might get their water supply from rivers which flow through several countries *[1 mark]* so they need to make sure that there is agreement between the different stakeholder countries about how the water will be managed *[1 mark]*.

d) This question is level marked. There are 4 extra marks available for spelling, punctuation and grammar.
How to grade your answer:

Level 0: There is no relevant information. *[0 marks]*

Level 1: There are a few points about how people have attempted to manage water resources sustainably. *[1-3 marks]*

Level 2: There is a clear examination of how people have attempted to manage water resources in countries at different levels of development. *[4-6 marks]*

Level 3: There is a detailed examination of how people have attempted to manage water resources sustainably in countries at different levels of development. *[7-8 marks]*

Make sure your spelling, punctuation and grammar are consistently correct, that your meaning is clear and that you use a range of geographical terms correctly *[0-4 marks]*. Your answer must refer to named examples of countries at different levels of development.
Here are some points your answer may include:

- A brief description of each of your chosen countries and their level of development.
- A brief description of the available water resources and challenges for sustainable management in each of your chosen countries.
- Examples of sustainable water management strategies in each country, and whether or not they have been successful.
- How the country's level of development has affected the strategies it has adopted and their success.
- How the combination of the different strategies improves sustainable water management.
- Your answer could refer to Kenya and the UK. Kenya is vulnerable to water shortages and has problems with access to improved sanitation and clean drinking water. Kenya has received support from international charities and organisations to improve its water infrastructure and help communities manage their water resources. In the UK there are problems with supply and demand imbalances and overconsumption. A combination of technologies, such as water meters, and rules about water use has helped people reduce their water consumption.

Geographical Investigations — Fieldwork

Pages 88-89: Fieldwork in a Physical Environment

1 a) Your answer should state your enquiry question and briefly outline the conclusions that you came to. Your conclusions should then be linked to an appropriate area of geography. E.g. I investigated how river discharge and channel landforms changed along part of the long profile of the river *[1 mark]*. I found that discharge in the middle course was 42% higher than in the upper course, and that the channel contained more meanders in the middle course *[1 mark]*. This helped me to understand how river processes and landforms are affected by distance of the river from its source *[1 mark]*.

b) i) The technique you describe should relate to quantitative physical geography data that you collected yourself, e.g. beach/river profiles / sediment analysis / soil analysis etc. Your answer should give a description of what you did, e.g. sample frequency, method of measurement etc.
E.g. I recorded beach profiles by following transect lines from the sea to the top of the beach *[1 mark]*. At consecutive points where the slope angle changed, I measured the distance between two ranging poles with a tape measure, and measured the angle between them using a clinometer *[1 mark]*.

Component 3: Geographical Investigations

ii) Your explanation should include why you collected the data and how it helped you answer your original question.
E.g. I analysed pebble size at different points along the river to find out how it changed due to attrition *[1 mark]*. I took a random sample of 10 pebbles at every site to make sure that the data collected was reliable *[1 mark]*. The data showed that pebble size decreased as the distance from the source of the river increased, so I was able to answer my original question *[1 mark]*.

c) i) The technique you describe should relate to qualitative data that you collected about the landforms present, e.g. taking photos / drawing sketches etc. Your answer should give a description of what you did, e.g. method used to record the landforms, location of sampling sites etc.
E.g. I recorded the river landforms present by drawing labelled field sketches of the river valley *[1 mark]*. I drew a sketch at one location in each of the upper, middle and lower courses of the river *[1 mark]*.

ii) The limitation could relate to e.g. any difficulties you encountered relating to the technique itself, the type of data that you obtained, or the assumptions that you had to make when recording the data.
E.g. I found it hard to get the scale right in each of the field sketches *[1 mark]*, so the sketches may not have been very accurate representations of the landforms present *[1 mark]*.

d) Your data presentation technique may be a map, e.g. a land use map or a dot map; a particular type of chart or graph, e.g. a dispersion graph, a pie chart or a scatter graph; or an annotated field sketch or photograph. The strengths could relate to how the variables are presented, the scales used, how the trends and patterns are presented, or how effective they are.
E.g. **Data presentation technique:** pie charts
Strengths: E.g. pie charts clearly show the proportion of each class of data investigated *[1 mark]*, so using a pie chart for each place makes it easy to see the patterns between different places *[1 mark]*. Pie charts allow a large amount of data to be summarised *[1 mark]*, so pie charts make the data easier to understand *[1 mark]*.

e) E.g. using a geology map helped me to select sites at which to collect data *[1 mark]*, because it showed where rock types of different levels of vulnerability to erosion are situated along the coast *[1 mark]*. / Using a flood risk map helped me to select sites at which to collect data *[1 mark]*, because it helped me to understand where different landforms might be found, e.g. levees *[1 mark]*.

f) Any one from: e.g. I calculated the mean velocity of the river at different points along its course *[1 mark]*. This helped me to draw the conclusion that the velocity of the river increases as it gets further away for its source *[1 mark]*. / I calculated the interquartile range for the pebbles I measured at each site along the beach *[1 mark]*. This helped me draw the conclusion that pebble size was most variable at the northern end of the beach *[1 mark]*. / I used a line of best fit to identify whether there was a correlation between the channel depth and velocity *[1 mark]*. This helped me to draw the conclusion that the velocity of the river increases as channel depth increases *[1 mark]*.

g) E.g. the lower course of the river passed through a small town *[1 mark]*, which was at risk of flooding *[1 mark]*. Flood barriers have been constructed along the parts of the river that flow through the areas most at risk *[1 mark]*.

h) This question is level marked. How to grade your answer:
Level 0: There is no relevant information. *[0 marks]*
Level 1: There is a basic evaluation of the results, but little or no attempt to form a judgement on their effectiveness in providing a conclusion. *[1-3 marks]*
Level 2: There is a clear evaluation of the results of the enquiry and an attempt to make a judgement about their effectiveness in reaching a valid conclusion. *[4-6 marks]*

Level 3: There is a detailed evaluation of the results of the enquiry and a clear judgement about their effectiveness in reaching a valid conclusion. *[7-8 marks]*
Here are some points your answer may include:
• A description of the results obtained in the investigation.
• The conclusions that could be drawn from the results obtained.
• Whether the conclusions drawn answer the original question of the enquiry.
• Any limitations that may have affected the reliability or accuracy of the results obtained, including the size of the samples used.
• An overall judgement as to whether or not the results enabled valid conclusions to be drawn.

Page 90: *Investigating River Landscapes*

1 a) E.g. **Item:** dog biscuit/orange *[1 mark]*
Reason: any one from: e.g. they float so you can take measurements from them *[1 mark]*. / They don't have much surface area above the water, so they are less likely to be affected by wind *[1 mark]*. / They biodegrade so the investigation won't harm the environment if the floats aren't caught *[1 mark]*.

b) E.g. the float got caught on something, e.g. a rock as it passed downstream *[1 mark]* so it took much longer for the float to reach the end of the timed section *[1 mark]*.

c) 255, 278, 279, 297, 302, 310, 315
Median = **297** s *[1 mark]*
To find the median, put all the numbers in your data set in size order. The median is just the middle value — in this case it's 297.

d) $\frac{315 + 255 + 278 + 310 + 302 + 279 + 297}{7} = \frac{2036}{7}$
Mean = **291** s (to the nearest second) *[1 mark]*
You may have written your answer to more significant figures — you'll still get a mark as long as it rounds to 291 s.

e) E.g. annotated photographs/field sketches could have been used *[1 mark]*, to record the landforms that are present in a particular location on the river, such as waterfalls, gorges, meanders etc *[1 mark]*.

Page 91: *Investigating Coastal Landscapes*

1 a) Any two from: e.g. the ranging poles may not have been held straight *[1 mark]*, affecting the angles recorded *[1 mark]*. / The ranging poles may sink into the sand *[1 mark]*, affecting the angles recorded *[1 mark]*. / It can be difficult to take accurate readings with a clinometer *[1 mark]*, so the readings might vary if different people take them *[1 mark]*. / It might be difficult to identify the low water mark *[1 mark]*, so the profile might start from different points at each sampling site *[1 mark]*. / The tide will be going in or out during the data collection *[1 mark]*, changing the point where measuring starts unless all profiles are taken at the same time by different groups *[1 mark]*. / The 5 m interval could include a break of slope *[1 mark]*, so the results wouldn't show the true profile *[1 mark]*.

b) E.g. she might have chosen points at regular intervals along the beach *[1 mark]*, to investigate how the cross-profile changes along the shore *[1 mark]*.
Her decision might also have been affected by accessibility and safety concerns.

c) Any one from: e.g. the student could annotate the graph *[1 mark]*, so that there was more information about the beach features at each location *[1 mark]*. / The student could add photographs of each location *[1 mark]*, so that the features of the beach at each location could easily be seen *[1 mark]*. / The student could include a map showing the location of each of the profiles *[1 mark]*, so that they could be linked to other geographical features *[1 mark]*.

d) E.g. more cross profiles could have been measured *[1 mark]* at equal intervals along the beach *[1 mark]*.

Component 3: Geographical Investigations

Pages 92-93: Fieldwork in a Human Environment

1 a) The technique you describe should relate to human geography data that you collected yourself. You need to explain why you used the technique, for example how it helped you to answer your original question and how it provided reliable and accurate data.

E.g. Technique: pedestrian numbers survey.
Explanation: The survey enabled me to identify the number of people visiting different locations, so I could see how popular different locations were *[1 mark]*. This helped me understand the differences in environmental quality in the area *[1 mark]*. / The tally chart I used in the survey meant that the results were numerical *[1 mark]*, so the data could be easily compared between sites *[1 mark]*.

b) You need to explain why the sampling technique you used was appropriate for the question/hypothesis you were investigating.
E.g. stratified sampling was used for the questionnaires so that the perceptions of people of different ages could be obtained *[1 mark]*. This meant my conclusions were representative of the population in general *[1 mark]*.

c) Any two from: e.g. walked in single file, facing oncoming traffic *[1 mark]* to reduce the risk of road traffic accidents *[1 mark]*. / Wore high visibility clothing *[1 mark]* to reduce the risk of road traffic accidents *[1 mark]*. / Worked in groups of at least three *[1 mark]* in case of accidents *[1 mark]*. / Wore appropriate clothing for the weather *[1 mark]* to avoid cold/heat illnesses *[1 mark]*.

d) E.g. census data allowed me to compare the annual earnings between different parts of the city *[1 mark]*, which helped me to assess how the affluence of an area was correlated to environmental quality *[1 mark]*.

e) The data source you choose to write about could be a primary or secondary source. Make sure you explain how it helps to answer your original question.
E.g. I could have used the internet to find data on how house prices in different parts of the city have changed over time *[1 mark]*. This would have helped me determine how the quality of life in that part of the city has been changing *[1 mark]*.

f) Your data presentation technique may be a map, e.g. a land use map or a dot map; a particular type of chart or graph, e.g. a dispersion graph, pie chart or a scatter graph; or an annotated field sketch or photograph.
E.g. I placed radial graphs showing the number of pedestrians at different times of the day onto an outline map of the whole area *[1 mark]*, which allowed multiple sets of data to be compared between the locations I studied *[1 mark]*.

g) The limitation could relate to how the variables are presented, the scales used, how the trends and patterns are presented, or how effective they are.
E.g. each annotated photograph only showed one point in time *[1 mark]*. The views might change throughout the day, e.g. some times of day will have more traffic, which the photographs did not show *[1 mark]*.

h) Your explanation should include how environmental quality is linked to changes in the area and what you concluded about this in the area you studied.
E.g. I took photos of different areas of the city which gave me information about environmental quality, such as the appearance of buildings and amount of green space *[1 mark]*. I found that there was a correlation between environmental quality and how land use had changed over time *[1 mark]*. The parts of the city with high levels of pollution tended to be areas that had experienced de-industrialisation *[1 mark]*. This led me to the conclusion that areas where industry has declined have been more negatively affected by changes in land use than other areas of the city that I studied *[1 mark]*.

i) This question is level marked. How to grade your answer:
Level 0: There is no relevant information. *[0 marks]*
Level 1: There are a few points about the suitability of the sites used. *[1-3 marks]*
Level 2: There is a clear evaluation of the suitability of the sites used and the answer attempts to come to a conclusion. *[4-6 marks]*
Level 3: There is a detailed evaluation of the suitability of the sites used and the answer comes to a clear conclusion. *[7-8 marks]*
Here are some points your answer may include:
- An outline of the sites used and the conclusions that could be drawn from the data collected there. Whether these sites gave a good overall representation of the study area, in order to draw conclusions that answered the original question.
- An outline of the limitations of the choice of data collection sites, and how they may have affected the validity of the conclusion.
- An overall conclusion about the choice of data collection sites in answering the research question.

Page 94: Investigating Changing Urban Areas

1 a) i) E.g. the sampling sites are evenly spread between the inner city and the CBD, with three sites in each zone *[1 mark]*. This is useful as it allows reliable comparisons to be made between the land uses in the different zones/it is easier to spot anomalies in the data *[1 mark]*.

ii) Any one from: e.g. record the land use at a greater number of sampling sites *[1 mark]* in order to give a larger data set to reduce the chance of anomalies affecting the conclusions of the investigation *[1 mark]*. / Record the land use over a more even geographical spread in the city (e.g. in the south-east parts of the CBD and inner city) *[1 mark]*, in order to better represent the whole area when drawing conclusions *[1 mark]*.

b) Any one from: e.g. census data *[1 mark]* / house price data *[1 mark]* / a map showing the locations of major industries *[1 mark]*.

c) E.g. the location of the river may have influenced the land use of nearby areas *[1 mark]*, e.g. sampling sites C and F are both situated close to the river and both have partly industrial land use functions *[1 mark]*.

Page 95: Investigating Changing Rural Areas

1 a) Any one from: e.g. it is based on subjective opinions *[1 mark]* rather than objective measurements, which would be more reliable *[1 mark]*. / The pedestrians' views could be affected by bias *[1 mark]*, e.g. if they are aware of a place's reputation, they might be likely to answer the questions in a way that fits in with that reputation *[1 mark]*.

b) E.g. the answers to question 2 could be presented as annotated photographs *[1 mark]* with the photographs showing the areas of the environment identified as needing improvement annotated with quotations from the interviews *[1 mark]*.

c) Any one from: e.g. photographs *[1 mark]* / traffic counts *[1 mark]* / pedestrian counts *[1 mark]*

d) Any one from: e.g. maps could be used *[1 mark]* to indicate areas most likely to be affected by pollution from e.g. traffic/industry *[1 mark]*. / Census data could be used *[1 mark]*, to show whether the age structure (e.g. the proportion of children, young professionals or elderly people) in an area has an effect on the quality of the environment *[1 mark]*.

Geographical Investigations — UK Challenges

Pages 98-99: Geographical Investigations — UK Challenges

1 a) B *[1 mark]*
b) i) 102.0% *[1 mark]*

$$\frac{257.4 - 127.4}{127.4} \times 100 = 102.04...$$

Round down to four significant figures = 102.0%

Component 3: Geographical Investigations

ii) 9.5 million *[1 mark]*
Work out the range by subtracting the lowest value from the highest value.
16.5 million − 7 million = 9.5 million

iii) B *[1 mark]*

c) E.g. tourism is a source of income to the UK economy, including in rural areas and National Parks — for example, in 2014, visitors to the Lake District spent £1.15 billion *[1 mark]*. Many of the UK's National Parks are located in the north and west of the UK *[1 mark]*, so developing tourism in National Parks could help increase income in these areas *[1 mark]*.

2 E.g. between 2013 and 2014, the percentage of SSSI habitats in a favourable condition decreased *[1 mark]*, and between 2014 and 2016 it remained the same *[1 mark]*.

3 a) E.g. ecosystems in National Parks, such as peat bogs on Dartmoor, can store large amounts of carbon *[1 mark]*. This means that protecting National Parks can prevent more carbon dioxide from being released into the atmosphere, where it would contribute to the enhanced greenhouse effect *[1 mark]*.

b) E.g. population increase can mean that more people are visiting National Parks/using National Parks for recreation *[1 mark]*. This can damage ecosystems in the National Parks, for example by increasing the amount of litter or increasing rates of erosion on footpaths *[1 mark]*.

4 a) 29.8% *[1 mark]*
29.3% + 31.7% + 30.0% + 28.3% = 119.3%
119.3% ÷ 4 = 29.825%
Round up to three significant figures = 29.8%

b) E.g. the National Parks in Figure 7 all have much lower population densities than England and Wales *[1 mark]*. They have a much older population, e.g. the median age of the National Parks is over ten years higher than the median age of England and Wales *[1 mark]*. The proportion of the population aged over 65 is also much higher in the National Parks than in England and Wales.

c) Any one reason in favour of development from: e.g. developing infrastructure could help people access services such as health care more easily *[1 mark]*. / Developing renewable energy production sites could help reduce the area's reliance on fossil fuels *[1 mark]*. / Developing industry could bring jobs to the area *[1 mark]*.
Any one reason against development from: e.g. developing resource extraction could harm ecosystems *[1 mark]*. / Developing industry could cause air and water pollution in the area *[1 mark]*. / Development of houses/renewable energy production sites/resource extraction could spoil the scenery *[1 mark]*.

d) This question is level marked. There are 4 extra marks available for spelling, punctuation and grammar.
How to grade your answer:

Level 0: There is no relevant information. *[0 marks]*

Level 1: There is a basic description of some advantages and disadvantages of developing National Parks for tourism. *[1-4 marks]*

Level 2: There is a clear discussion of whether National Parks should be developed for tourism, which uses evidence from the Figures and other knowledge. *[5-8 marks]*

Level 3: There is a detailed and balanced discussion of whether National Parks should be developed for tourism, which uses evidence from the Figures and other knowledge to support a clear conclusion. *[9-12 marks]*

Make sure your spelling, punctuation and grammar are consistently correct, that your meaning is clear and that you use a range of geographical terms correctly *[0-4 marks]*.
You must use your own knowledge and information from pages 96-97 to discuss the arguments for and against the development of tourism in the UK's National Parks.
It doesn't matter which way you argue, as long as you consider both sides and use evidence to justify your arguments.

Here are some points your answer may include:

- A brief introduction to the issue, e.g. what National Parks are and why they are popular with tourists.
- How tourism in National Parks can benefit local people, e.g. tourism can provide jobs and income to areas in and around National Parks. Developing infrastructure and services for tourists, such as improving public transport connections, can also help local people.
- How tourism in National Parks can improve health and wellbeing, e.g. by allowing people to spend time outdoors and close to nature, which can reduce their risk of developing certain health problems.
- How tourism in National Parks can help with conservation, e.g. tourism provides income that can be used for conservation. If tourists are visiting National Parks to see wildlife and undeveloped landscapes, then this provides an incentive to protect wildlife and landscapes in National Parks. Tourism can also provide a way of educating people about wildlife in National Parks and encourage people to volunteer to help with conservation projects.
- How tourism in National Parks can negatively impact local people, e.g. tourism could cause house prices in the area to rise and increase road traffic, contributing to air and noise pollution. Promoting tourism can put pressure on National Parks to keep ecosystems looking attractive, which can restrict other ways of managing the National Parks, such as farming or building homes for local people.
- How tourism in National Parks can negatively impact ecosystems, e.g. walkers and cyclists can cause soil erosion around footpaths, trample vegetation and disturb wildlife. Many National Parks currently have low population densities, but developing them for tourism and increasing the number of opportunities in the area could increase the local population, which could put more pressure on local ecosystems.
- A brief conclusion that states whether on balance you think that National Parks should be developed for tourism, supported by evidence from the body of your answer.

Remember, to get full marks you must support your answer with evidence from the figures. For example, if you argued for developing National Parks for tourism, you might have used evidence about the money spent by visitors in National Parks (Figure 3), which shows that tourism can generate income for National Parks.

CGP

ISBN 978 1 78908 303 3

9 781789 083033

GEAQA41   £2.00
                (Retail Price)

www.cgpbooks.co.uk